THE PROMETHEUS PROJECT

Gerald Feinberg, Professor of Physics at Columbia University, received his B.A., M.A. and Ph.D. degrees from Columbia. He has spent a year at the Institute for Advanced Study in Princeton, two years at Brookhaven Laboratories, and a year at Rockefeller University in New York City. He has written on various aspects of physics for *Scientific American, Annual Review of Nuclear Science, Physical Review, Science et Vie* and other technical publications.

The Prometheus Project

MANKIND'S SEARCH
FOR LONG-RANGE GOALS

Gerald Feinberg

ANCHOR BOOKS
DOUBLEDAY & COMPANY, INC.
GARDEN CITY, NEW YORK

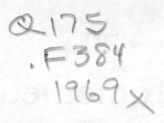

The Prometheus Project was
published by Doubleday & Company, Inc.
in a hardcover edition in January 1969.

Anchor Books Edition: 1969

Contents

Preface

The origin of this book was a discussion group that I organized in New York in the fall of 1962. The discussions, which took place weekly for several months, were concerned with possible long-range goals for the human race, and with possible future developments in technology. The small group included natural scientists, social scientists, philosophers, and their wives, and therefore basically was restricted to the academic community. The most valuable ideas that emerged from these discussions were critical analyses of some of the suggested goals, and a study of some problems that could develop for society as a result of aging control. These have strongly influenced the views I have expressed in Chapters III and V of this book.

The first discussion group was not as successful in producing new goals to consider as we would have liked, and it therefore appeared that to get any further a much wider group of people would have to be stimulated to think about the idea. Nothing along these lines was attempted, however, until late in 1966, when I spent a year at the Rockefeller University in New York. During that time, conversations with Dr. Rollin Hotchkiss convinced me that the pace of developments in molecular biology was so rapid that the possibility of biological engineering was almost upon us. Since I believe that this is one of the areas in which agreement on long-range goals is necessary for rational decision, I felt that it was crucial to get started on the road to such agreement as quickly as possible. I therefore began writing this book, with the advice and encouragement of Dr. Hotchkiss. The book was essentially completed during my stay at Rockefeller University, to whose hospitality I therefore owe a deep debt of gratitude. The book has been written with the basic purpose of convincing as many people as possible of the need for long-range goals. I have tried to keep the line of argument as simple as I could, so that others than scientists and philosophers would be able to follow it. I have therefore entered into very few technical details about either science or philosophy, and I believe that such details are unnecessary for the main thrust of the argument.

There are two other groups of people whom it is a pleasure to thank for their help. One is the regular participants in the first discussion group. These were Jeremy Bernstein, Mr. and Mrs. Lowell Dworin, Arnold Faden, Irwin Friedman, Michael Hart, Sidney Morgenbesser, Mr. and Mrs. Harrison Roth, Mr. and Mrs. Joe Rothberg, Barbara Sakitt, Robert Shapiro, and Mr. and Mrs. Menasha Tausner. If the Prometheus Project ever succeeds, all of them should feel that their interest helped it at a crucial time.

It is also a pleasure to thank those who have read various stages of this manuscript and given me their very useful advice about ways in which it could be improved. In many cases, this advice has played a major role in the writing and re-writing of the book. For this my thanks are due to Jeremy Bernstein, Evan Cooper, Arnold Faden, my father Leon Feinberg, Lillian Hartmann, Mr. and Mrs. Rollin Hotchkiss, Sidney Morgenbesser, Ernest Nagel, Abraham Pais, Mr. and Mrs. Joel Pincus, Barbara Sakitt, Dennis Sciama, Mr. and Mrs. Robert Shapiro, Barbara Silberdick Feinberg, Mr. and Mrs. Russell Targ, William Targ, and Mr. and Mrs. Menasha Tausner.

I would like to thank Irene Tramm for her splendid work in typing the manuscript from my often indecipherable writing. Finally, I wish to thank my editor, Anne Freedgood, for her encouragement and her many useful suggestions for reordering and rephrasing the text.

Gerald Feinberg
NEW YORK
JANUARY 1968

THE PROMETHEUS PROJECT

I. The Need for Long-Range Goals

This book is devoted to a question that has not been in intellectual fashion for some time: "What should be the goals of the human race?" In this introductory chapter I hope to convince the reader of several propositions relating to this question. The main points to be made here are the following:

1. The long-range goals of the human race have so far not been reconsidered in the light of the scientific discoveries of the past few hundred years, and it is essential that they be.

2. Because of the increasing rate of technological advance, we will soon be faced with literally "world-shaking decisions," which can be rationally made only if we know something about our long-range goals.

3. An agreement on long-range goals might help to alleviate some of the present disagreements over more immediate issues, which may otherwise lead to the early destruction of the human race.

On the basis of these propositions, it is clear that a new inquiry into our long-range goals is imperative. The purpose of this book is to propose a group effort, which I call the Prometheus Project (from the Greek word *prometheus,* meaning foresight), by which humanity can choose its goals. These should not be imposed on an unwilling population from above, but rather be the choice of free men. In that way, humanity would move closer to becoming the shaper of its own destiny.

This first chapter presents the main themes to be considered in the book, without treating them in depth. Some more-detailed arguments will be found in later chapters, and in the references at the end. For the most part, however, I have tried to be more descriptive than analytic in the presentation.

Let us then consider the kind of society that is evolving on earth, why it needs long-range goals, and how it may obtain them.

THE UNITY OF MANKIND

Most civilized people in modern times have come to believe in the essential unity of mankind. This unity means that the constant factors in our genetic heritage and in our upbringing imply similarities in our aspirations and in the process of our lives. While these latter similarities may be somewhat masked by the obvious differences imposed by life in diverse human environments, many features of our common humanity stand out above the variations.

The phrase, unity of mankind, also describes some aspects of the long-term evolution of societies, which takes place in two ways. With the improvement in transportation and communication, relatively homogeneous societies, such as the United States or western Europe, have developed among sizable fractions of the world's population. These same factors also tend to diminish the differences between the distinct societies that still exist. It therefore seems a fairly safe prediction that within the foreseeable future the differences will have become so small that there will be in effect a single society inhabiting the world.

Furthermore, a process of equalization has been going on within existing societies. In most societies today, increased equality among the members is considered a theoretically desirable goal, and, by most standards, such as distribution of income, amount of education, typical daily activities, etc., members of the industrially developed societies have actually been approaching such equality. This does not mean that differences do not exist or will not continue to exist between people in a society, but rather that most options available to any member of the group will become available to any other member, and that the decision between such options will be a matter of choice, rather than of predetermination.

LONG-RANGE GOALS

Once the unity of mankind is accepted, the question arises as to whether mankind as a group should have any long-range goals, and if so, what these goals should be. This question is less apparent if one does not recognize the essential similarities among human beings, and indeed most past thinkers who have been concerned with long-term goals have recognized them.

By a long-range goal, I mean some desired future state of affairs whose realization would require an effort lasting over many generations. For example, a possible long-range goal would be the spread of the human race beyond the confines of earth to other stellar systems, either for exploration or for eventual inhabitation of them. Because of the immense distances between the stars, such expansion of human society, if at all possible, would require a great many years to carry out by any methods we can imagine.[1]

To qualify as a long-range goal of mankind, the goal must involve a large number of people, probably a considerable fraction of the human race. There are two ways in which many people could be involved. Their direct efforts might be required to bring about the goal—if, for example, the goal were a society in which we all know ourselves and love our neighbors. Alternatively, the goal might have an important effect on everybody's life when it was realized, even though the direct efforts of many people are not required to bring it about. This might be the case if we chose as a goal the elimination of as much suffering as possible through the biological reconstruction of the human race to remove some of the causes of this suffering. Or they might be involved in both ways, as they have been in a goal that has been sought partly consciously for several millennia—the transformation of the earthly environment from its natural state to one more suitable for human habitation. Some people believe that this goal has recently been renounced through such by-products of industrialization and population increase as air pollution, destruction of the scenery, etc. On balance, however, it seems clear that the world in 1968 is a much safer and pleasanter place for human habitation than it was in 10,000 B.C.

Many worth-while goals do not qualify as goals for humanity under this criterion, because they involve the efforts of, and are of interest to, a relatively small number of people. An example of this is the continuing attempt to understand the relations among natural phenomena, which has been until now confined to a small number of scientists, although its technological by-products do have a wider application. It may be that goals of this kind qualify as general human goals under the broader criterion that most people approve of the activity, even though they are not directly concerned with it. But such vicarious goals will not be stressed in these considerations.

The formulation of long-range human goals requires definite ideas about the nature of the world, man, and the relation between the two. For that reason, the goals of mankind have received much attention from religious thinkers. Most of the major religions have emphasized specific goals as central to human life on earth. In some cases, these have been individual goals, such as the Buddhist aim of avoidance of suffering. In other cases, the goals are collective efforts,

such as the glorification of God through good
works and the conversion of heathens.

We should realize that the goals expressed by
the various religions were first formulated many
centuries ago when our knowledge about the
natural world was quite primitive compared to
our present knowledge. It is reasonable to expect
that the new things we have learned should
have some influence on the goals we consider.
This has, however, not occurred, at least explicitly. Religious men have for the most part
worked under the assumption that the goals were
conclusively determined long ago. They have not
found it necessary to investigate whether these
goals are consistent with the new knowledge. A
notable exception to this has been the attempt by
Teilhard de Chardin to analyze the question of
man's ultimate end within a religious framework,
but in the light of evolutionary biology. As with
many efforts to unite seemingly orthogonal
views, the proponents of each side seem unhappy
with this marriage, but some of Teilhard's conclusions are quite interesting and will be discussed
later.

Most naturalist thinkers, on the other hand,
have avoided the question of ultimate goals altogether, either by emphasizing the means by which
things are to be accomplished, or by concentrat-
ing on more immediate ends such as the reform
of some specific aspect of society. One reason for
this is that once a religious framework is rejected,
most people believe there is no source outside of
man to prescribe what the goals should be, and

the choice appears arbitrary. I do not think that this argument is relevant. Whatever the source of a proposed goal, the choice of whether to accept it remains with man, and must be made on the basis of his reason and his feelings. If such a choice need be made, it is irresponsible to refuse to make it because the answer is not written in the stars.

Indeed, another attitude toward the setting of goals seems more justified. In the absence of man, or creatures like him, the universe possesses neither awareness nor plan. Just as the emergence of human consciousness has finally enabled matter to become aware of itself, so a decision by the human race about its goals would provide a plan or purpose for at least our part of the universe. In providing this we would be exercising imagination, anticipation, and will—in short, the qualities of mind that man alone possesses in the known world. To refuse this challenge of providing something entirely new in the world would be to fall somewhat short of our full humanity.

There have been exceptions to the rule that naturalistic thinkers have been unwilling to speculate about man's ultimate goals. One group of exceptions is certain philosophers of the Enlightenment, such as Condorcet. These writers, while rejecting much of religions and the goals suggested by them, nevertheless thought of some sort of Natural Law as prescribing the direction in which man should go, and for the most part were quite optimistic about his prospects.

There are also some exceptions to the rule of disinterest in long-range goals among the writers of imaginative fiction. Olaf Stapledon, in particular, has given penetrating treatments of some possible futures of mankind,[2] in which definite choices about ultimate goals are involved either explicitly or implicitly. It is unfortunate that these imaginative writings have not been given much serious attention, since they are not only a fertile source of suggestions for goals, but also often point out unexpected implications that the attainment of some goal might have for human life.

Granting that the ultimate goals of mankind have not been a primary concern of late, one can reasonably ask whether it is not a good thing that men operate on a short-term basis and do not try to chart the distant future. Plausible arguments can indeed be given for this point of view,[3] and the spirit behind it has been responsible for much of human progress. Nevertheless, in this book I intend to make a case for the view that a discussion of the long-term goals of man is not only feasible, but of crucial importance for dealing with the problems arising from the new possibilities to be afforded us by science and technology in the near future.

THE IMPENDING
"WORLD-SHAKING" DECISIONS

The critical necessity of a discussion of long-term goals is a result of two factors: the growing interdependence of different parts of the world society, and the rapid development of technology. The combination of these produces a situation in which actions or decisions by a small group can produce large-scale, irreversible effects that were neither expected nor desired by their initiators. An example of this is the effect of fallout from nuclear tests. It was not originally expected that this would be a serious problem, and even after the phenomenon was recognized, a long controversy ensued about the possible genetic results of the increased radioactivity of the environment. Eventually, concern over these effects played an important role in producing the treaty banning atmospheric tests, a by-product which was hardly in the minds of those originally planning the tests. Another example is the substantial pollution of the atmosphere in many cities, produced by the large-scale use of automobiles in the twentieth century. This result was neither anticipated nor desired by the inventors and manufacturers of automobiles.

In the near future, technological possibilities will grow to the point where individuals or small groups could take actions that would result in a radical transformation of human life. Take, for example, the construction of intelligent, self-improving machines. This development has been considered technically feasible by many workers in the field, who point out that there is no known reason why such machines could not become more intelligent than human beings.[4] This point, which is somewhat controversial, will be considered in detail in Chapter III. Even a conclusive demonstration of the possibility of such machines would have an immense influence on the human outlook and on the motivation of human creativity. The actual construction of such machines would, of course, influence not only the way people think but also their daily lives. These influences would be qualitatively different from those of previous technological developments, since they would involve nonhuman patterns of thought and perhaps of will. Prudence would therefore suggest that the development of such machines should be preceded by an attempt to analyze its consequences.

In order to evaluate such consequences, a knowledge of what the machines can do is insufficient. It is necessary to know also what purposes are served in making them, and other aims with which their existence might conflict. Intelligent machines might be able to carry out a large part of the creative thought now done by humans, more efficiently than it is done at present. The opportunity to think creatively is, however, a primary source of happiness for many people, who would lose much of their motivation if such thought became unnecessary for them. It is precisely this kind of conflict that can be resolved only with some kind of knowledge of the long-term goals mankind wishes to pursue. If the effects of some action can strongly influence mankind as a whole, then the aims relevant to deciding about the action should be those of mankind, and not those of a small group.

Thoughtful scientists and others have, of

course, recognized that some of the new possibilities opened to us by technology will require ethical choices too far-reaching to be made purely on the basis of immediate aims.[5] I am here simply amplifying this by pointing out that the ethical principles on which such a choice must be based are intimately connected with the question of ultimate human goals, which should therefore be explicitly considered before the choice is made.

I have spoken of certain decisions as having irreversible effects. By this I mean that because of the rapidity and completeness of the change induced by certain actions, whole areas of human activity or possible alternative developments could become inaccessible. Later on, I will analyze some of these "irreversible" decisions in detail. For the present, it is enough to realize that if such situations may in principle occur it is an additional urgent reason for the analysis of the consequences of actions, which was not present in the past, when no human action could really foreclose a whole set of possibilities into the indefinite future. Again, the making of irreversible decisions requires some idea of where the human race wants to go, since otherwise one cannot know how important the possibilities opened up are compared to those eliminated.

The advent of "world-shaking decisions" thus calls for some kind of long-range planning of the future of mankind. Otherwise man, having elevated himself through his technology from being the plaything of blind nature, might become the victim of blind actions on his own part.

THE BENEFITS OF SETTING
LONG-TERM GOALS

There is another respect in which some agreement on the goals of humanity could play an important role. It could provide some meeting ground between otherwise opposing groups. The present world situation has been aggravated by the theory, held by each side, that the people on the other side are malevolent or diabolic. As a result, it has often appeared that world politics is a "zero sum game," in which any positive achievement by one side, such as a successful space probe of Venus, is necessarily a loss for the other side. This is surely not the case. Since men share a common biology, as well as some elements of a common upbringing and culture, there must be some long-term goals on which we can agree with the Communists, or on which any antagonistic groups might agree.

The mutual recognition of such aims would suggest the possibility of joint actions to promote them. Perhaps more important, an analysis by differing groups of their long-term goals could lead to a recognition of the relative unimportance of some of the immediate disagreements that now seem worth fighting over. If some such process does not occur, it seems likely that the world will face a series of future crises as a result of technological advances by many countries with irreconcilable interests. One such crisis might then lead to a particular irreversible action—the destruction of humanity.

In addition to whatever other ends are served by thinking about the goals of mankind, the activity itself should be a spiritually ennobling one to those undertaking it. A greater concern for the welfare of those who will be born long after us would be an important step in the progression of feeling from self to family to nation to the world.

Another possible benefit is that some will find in the search for goals a contribution to the parallel but distinct search for meaning in their own lives. In fact, this need for direction in the life of an individual is one of the important elements in human psychology that must be considered in formulating goals for the race. I will return to the question of the relation between goals for humanity and the desire of individuals to find meaning for their lives later, when discussing the human condition.

A final inducement to entering into a search for long-range goals is the intellectual adventure involved in such an inquiry. While the choice of goals is to some extent a matter of feeling, an understanding of the alternatives requires, among other things, an appreciation of some scientific ideas about the world that is not common, even among scientists. What is required for this is not a detailed understanding of the content of each science, but rather a kind of synthesis of many different strands from many sciences. A formulation of this type of synthesis is likely to appeal to a different kind of mind than that of the active research worker, which does not make it any less difficult or valuable. When this synthesis is achieved, it could well bring the excitement of scientific discovery to many who have remained unmoved by the detailed accomplishments of the individual sciences.

The application of any goal to specific decisions involves making predictions about developments in the somewhat distant future. The ability to do this successfully is not in very great supply. Whatever the reason for this, once people begin thinking about long-term goals, it is likely to make much more common a "long view" of the human race and its prospects, and this in turn will return prophecy to its honorable place as a human activity. One may hope that this will lead to an improvement in the accuracy of the predictions that are made.

MORE IMMEDIATE PROBLEMS

In calling for more attention to be paid to long-term goals, I do not mean to slight those concerned with more immediate problems. The elimination of the many forms of needless misery in the world is likely to be a preoccupation of men for the foreseeable future. It is understandably difficult for many people to become concerned about distant goals when people are starving and the survival of humanity is by no means assured.

My own concern with more remote problems is based on an optimistic estimate that most of our immediate problems will be solved in a relatively short time by the march of technology and the worldwide spread of those aspects of Western cul-

ture that are responsible for our high living standards. The problem of subsistence seems to be essentially solved in the United States and western
Europe, and the most pressing problems within
those societies may soon be those relating to sur-
plus production. As I will indicate, in the discussion of the near future in a subsequent chapter,
I think that this will be the case for the whole
world in the next century. In the longer run, a
failure to decrease the birth rate could again
raise the problem of subsistence, but some form
of birth control seems likely to remove that con-
tingency. Since I regard such problems as relatively short term I will not deal with them in any
detail here.

THE PROMETHEUS PROJECT

If one is convinced that there is a need for agreement on long-range goals for humanity, the first
question is how such goals are to be found. One
obvious source is the goals that have been proposed in the past. As I have said, most of these
were formulated before the present scientific view
of nature and man was available. I believe that a
proper appreciation of the content of science is
essential for the expression of goals that have
some chance of being relevant for the future. Although it may well be true that facts do not imply
values, they do place restrictions on what values
are relevant to the world. Therefore I am not
convinced that the principles of the leading ethical and religious thinkers of two thousand years

ago provide the goals that we will wish to agree on. Nevertheless, after presenting some of the aspects of science relevant to human goals, I will attempt to summarize some of the long-range goals that have been proposed in the past and to analyze them critically in the light of this knowledge.

If the goals proposed in the past are insufficient for the future, we have no choice but to think of new ones. I have followed a habit of technologists, who like to refer their activities back to the ancients, and have called this attempt to find new goals the Prometheus Project.

The Prometheus Project cannot be an effort of one man, or of a small number of men, since no small group can encompass the total wisdom or feelings of mankind. I am writing in the hope of stimulating enough interest in these questions so that eventually a sizable fraction of the human race will take part in the discussion that leads to the goals that are finally accepted. It is both just and prudent that the formulation of goals that are supposed to apply to all humanity should be a joint effort of as much of the human race as wishes to take part in it. If there are no institutions through which such a joint effort, involving perhaps hundreds of millions of people, could be carried out, then we must create the necessary institutions as we go along, as another means to the end.

Because I think it is necessary that the goals of humanity proceed from all of humanity, it is not the primary purpose of this book to suggest goals. The goals that will be described are mainly illustrative, and I do not think it likely that they will be the ones to be adopted. What I will do here is some of the analytical work that will be helpful in the choice, that is, study some questions of logical principle that should be answered in order better to understand any proposed goals. This subject might be called the philosophy of goals and includes questions such as, "Should we, the people alive today, bind the people of the future to our own purposes, and can we do so?" While it is possible to agree on goals without knowing how to answer such questions, it is not clear that we would know the implications of what had been decided, and an unclear goal is unlikely to be of help in determining what path to take in order to reach it.

One such philosophical question is sufficiently important to bear mentioning here. This has to do with the amount of diversity that will be possible when a consensus on long-range goals is reached. I see no reason why such goals need be unique or categorical. In particular, we may wish to consider a number of goals simultaneously, as long as they are not contradictory, and we can assign some order of priority to their acomplishment. Furthermore, it seems likely to me that most of the goals we will consider would not completely determine the lives of all members of society, either during their accomplishment or afterwards. Therefore I do not believe that the adoption of such goals need lead to a serious curtailment of individual freedom. Finally, the very process of working toward distant goals may require some social experimentation in order to understand whether we really desire the situation envisaged in our goals. Thus, it is possible that the consideration of long-range goals may lead to an increased diversity in society, at least in the short run.

II. Where We Stand

In order to help us choose our goals, that is, decide where we would like to go, it is useful to have some idea about where we are now, and about the general terrain and modes of travel that are open to us. That is, it is important to know what things about man's present life seem particularly desirable or undesirable to him, in order to recognize which things we should strive to enhance, and which to eliminate. It is also important to know those things about the natural world that might constrain the goals we choose, or might be used to help us achieve these goals.

Analyses of the way things are for man on earth have been given many times, and most of the positions that have been defined long ago are still descriptive of at least a part of the human condition today. A new element is that we will soon have the option of changing man if we choose. On the other hand, it is only in the twentieth century that we have reached the stage in our scientific understanding of the world where we can be confident that our choice of goals will not suffer seriously from a lack of such understanding. It is this development that opens the way for us to formulate goals that are in accordance with the laws of nature, and that are therefore relevant and attainable. We will see later that ancient philosophies and religions did not have this understanding of the world, and their goals suffered accordingly. While there are doubtless gaps in our own picture of nature, they are much smaller than in the past, and there is reason to believe that the gaps are mostly irrelevant to human life.

This section will therefore be devoted to a description of some aspects of the present state of scientific knowledge, to an outline of a few gaps in that knowledge, and to some comments about flaws in the present human condition.

THE SCIENTIFIC BACKGROUND

In the four thousand years that have elapsed since the first recorded scientific speculations, our understanding of the world has progressed to the point where we now have a detailed picture of how most nonliving phenomena occur, and we are rapidly extending the picture to include living things as well. Most of the progress has occurred in the last four hundred years, since Galileo and Newton used mathematical models to describe some aspects of nature successfully. The twentieth century has produced some of the most spectacular advances in scientific understanding, in particular the quantum theory of the atom, the molecular description of living processes, and the recognition of the immense size and duration of the visible universe.

While the discoveries of Newton and his followers have been known long enough for their significance to become appreciated by a large group of educated men, this is not yet the case for much of twentieth-century science. Yet I think that some of the recent discoveries have important consequences for human goals, and that they are sufficiently well founded to endure in any future science. These discoveries can be described in the form of a series of general principles that are abstracted from them. I will not give the detailed evidence that leads to these principles, but the interested reader can find this in the references.

The principles can all be stated fairly succinctly and do not require a training in science to be understood. It is at least partly the fault of scientists that the insights they have obtained have often seemed mysterious and incomprehensible to nonscientists. I hope that the reader will not find this to be the case with these propositions.

1. All forms of matter are made of a few basic constituents, and the same general laws of physics describe all natural phenomena from atoms to stars, including men.

2. The characteristic activities of living things are the result of the same kind of physical and chemical processes as are found in nonliving things. This very probably includes human mental activities.

3. There is no indication of any plan in the development of natural phenomena. The present complexity of living things has evolved from a much simpler condition through the random process of natural selection via the survival of the well-adapted organisms.

4. The universe is immense in size and extremely old by the measures of human spaces and times. Hence it is unlikely that the universe is made for man, or that he has been chosen to be its central theme.

5. Many of the forms of human behavior are not inborn but rather are learned. Specific behavior patterns can be changed by psychological, chemical, and physical methods. Human nature is therefore not something unalterable but can be changed.

Science has not yet, of course, answered all questions about the natural world, and at the end of the chapter I will outline some of the open scientific questions that may be relevant to human goals. But let us now somewhat amplify the propositions that science has given us in order to see their relevance to the study of our long-range goals.

The Universality of Physics and Chemistry

One general principle suggested by the science of the twentieth century is that everything in the world is made of the same basic constituents. These are a few tiny objects, known as elementary particles, that have certain definite properties such as mass and electric charge. The particles composing matter are neutrons, protons, and electrons. If a piece of any kind of matter is viewed with sufficiently high magnification (which requires other kinds of illumination than visible light), it will be found to be composed of these particles. The diversity of forms that matter takes on to us is partly due to the scale of our perceptions. If we could view matter directly on a scale of a billionth of a centimeter, all forms of matter would look very similar. The various types of matter differ only in the relative number of each kind of particle and the arrangements of the particles in space. There is no other difference in the composition of living or dead matter, or between the matter on earth and in other parts of the known universe.

Furthermore, the same general laws of physics and chemistry apply to all natural phenomena from atoms to stars, including men. Man is what he is because of physical law and not in spite of it. What sets us apart from inanimate matter is not that we are made of different stuff, or that different physical principles determine our workings. It is rather the greater complexity of our construction and the self-awareness that this makes possible.

One consequence of this universality of physical laws is that through our understanding of these laws, we can modify and control natural phenomena. While man is not the pampered child of a benevolent Mother Nature, neither is he a toy in the hands of malevolent and irresistible forces. The way things happen is designed neither to favor man nor to frustrate him. If man chooses to modify nature in any way that is possible, the only resistance he will encounter is the sometimes unforeseen consequences of his acts. If one views this effort to remake the world as a struggle between man and nature, then one must recognize that nature neither knows nor cares, while man does, and therein lies his advantage.

The Continuity between the Living and the Nonliving

A particularly important application of the universality of physics and chemistry comes with the realization that life is the result of a complicated set of processes that are physical and chemical transformations. Over a period of two centuries, the characteristic properties of living things have been systematically related to known properties of inorganic matter. This began in 1828, when urea, a chemical hitherto produced only by animals, was synthesized from inorganic chemicals. The latest step in this development has been the understanding of heredity and replication, two of the fundamental life processes, in terms of the properties of a set of related chemical compounds known as DNA. Although DNA is a very complex molecule compared to water or salt, its properties seem to follow from standard chemical and physical laws, and human heredity is in that sense similar to the rusting of iron or the fermentation of wine. The success of the molecular approach to heredity has so impressed most biologists that James Watson, a co-discoverer of the DNA theory has written,[1] "Complete certainty now exists among essentially all biochemists that the other characteristics of living organisms (for example, selective permeability across cell membranes, muscle contraction, and the hearing and memory processes) will all be completely understood in terms of the coordinative interactions of large and small molecules." This sentence may serve as the credo of molecular biology.

If the physiological aspects of life are explicable in terms of physics and chemistry, it is likely that human mental processes are as well. Conceivably, the situation might be otherwise, and there might be some phenomena involved in the human mind that are not found elsewhere in the world. In that case, it would be necessary to extend physics to include the new phenomena as well.[2] However, the continuity of structure and function from nonliving matter to living and from the simplest forms of life to the most complicated strongly suggests that even the most characteristic human activities such as thought and consciousness have an explanation, as yet only partly known, in chemical and physical phenomena.[3]

To the extent that man's attributes are determined by his physical and chemical structure, man can be modified in the same sense that any other physical system can be modified. Provided that man can understand how he works, he can try to improve his workings in specific ways. Whether or not "human nature" can be changed by education, upbringing, or other cultural factors, the possibility of changing human nature by changing human biology is a new factor that must now be considered by molders of society.

The Absence of Plan in Nature

To many men who have speculated about natural processes, in particular those involving living creatures, it has seemed inconceivable that things could be as they are without the operation in nature of some external direction or plan.[4] Many examples of structure and function in animals, such as the remarkable working of the eye, or the fact that the earth falls within the small range of temperatures at which biological activity occurs, have been cited in support of this view. Yet scientific analysis finds no trace of plan in natural phenomena, living or nonliving, as they take place, but only the laws of physics and chemistry.

It has been suggested that a plan might be involved only in the change from simpler to more complex organisms, and that a real problem for science is to account for how such complicated and well-adapted organisms as now exist could have come about, starting with simple elements. The answer to the problem stated in this form was provided in the nineteenth century by Darwin's theory of evolution, and in particular by the concept of natural selection. The basis of this concept is by now well known. Darwin assumed that there was some mechanism producing small differences among otherwise similar living things. These differences imply that in any given environment, one creature will be better adapted for survival than another. On a purely statistical basis, more of these will survive to reproduce themselves. Darwin further assumed that there was some way by which the differences leading to greater survival could be passed on to the descendants of the original creature. In this way, after a sufficient lapse of time, all of the creatures living would probably be descended from the originally favored ones, and would, in the particular feature that they shared with their ancestor, be adapted to their environment, providing that it had not changed in that time.

The twentieth century has provided magnificent confirmation for these ideas. Many physical phenomena in the environment such as radiation, heat, and some chemicals have been found to be capable of causing variations among examples of an organism. The method for passing on these differences is the remarkable property of the DNA molecule that is known as self-replication, or making a copy of itself, which it controls by purely chemical means. The phenomenon of selective adaptation to the environment has been demonstrated directly by producing bacteria that are resistant to penicillin from cultures containing bacteria that were originally mostly unresistant, simply by growing the bacteria in a medium containing penicillin so that only the few resistant bacteria could survive and propagate.[5] Although it has not yet been shown that the rate of mutation and adaptation accounts for the time scale of biological evolution, there is little reason to doubt that this is so.

Natural selection thus removes the necessity

for assuming any plan in nature by stating that creatures are in approximate harmony with their environment because the harmonious are more likely to survive. If one asks how it is that so many examples of successful adaptation are actually found, the reply must be that the successful creatures represent a very small fraction of the total number of trials. If it is further suggested that a plan may exist in nature outside of man without having yet manifested itself to us, we are free to answer, following Laplace, that we have no need of that hypothesis.

As remarkable as the results of natural selection are, from the point of view of humanity it is by no means the most desirable method for producing change, for at least three reasons. First, it works too slowly for man to see results in his own species. Second, it is limited in the environments to which it can enable creatures to adapt, at least if the environment is changed too rapidly. For example, it is unlikely that any living organisms could adapt through natural selection to a sudden rise of one thousand degrees in the average temperature of the earth. Finally, and most important, man has his own ideas about what characteristics are desirable, and these are not necessarily the ones that natural selection will produce.

Man, being conscious, can provide a direction for the development of natural phenomena, and, being intelligent, can often take a more direct route to a desired end than natural selection would, even if the same goal were reached. Thus the invention of the telescope provided a much more immediate solution to the problem of seeing distant objects than awaiting a human mutation with telescopic vision would have. Hence there is no reason why we should wait for evolution to bring about those changes in man that we desire. If we can only agree on our goals, our technology can do the rest.

The Place of the Earth in the Universe

Our estimate of the size and time scale of the universe has increased progressively with the development of astronomy from the fifteenth century until the present. The size of that portion of the universe visible to our instruments bears about the same relation to the size of the earth as the earth does to the size of a typical atom. This entire region of space is filled uniformly with loose collections of stars, known as galaxies, separated from one another by a distance of about ten times their size. If one thinks of the stars in a galaxy as analogous to the atoms in a gas, then the density of stars corresponds to a much more rarefied vacuum than has been attained on earth. As a result, the stars do not influence one another very much in a developed galaxy, although they may do so in an earlier stage in the evolution of a galaxy.

In addition to the stars, the universe is known to contain a large amount of dust and free atoms. It is thought by many astronomers that this additional matter slowly coalesces into new galaxies, or new stars within a galaxy. The time taken by this process can be used as an estimate of the age of a galaxy and appears to be some tens of billions of years. This is a few times the age of the earth, as estimated by radioactive dating, which is about six billion years. This in turn is five to ten times the age of the oldest remains of living things found on earth. There are reasons to expect that our galaxy, the solar system, and the earth will continue to exist without major changes for a time in the future comparable to their present age, that is for some billions of years.

In comparison to these times, the five thousand years of recorded human history, or even the million years or so that human life has existed on earth, is very short indeed. Apparently man has a much longer future in store for him than he has had a past, providing he does not destroy himself.

These facts about space and time do not imply that man is insignificant and unworthy, but rather reiterate that there is no grand design for the world, of which humanity is the culmination. The scale of the universe is far too great for man to be its central theme. If we are ever to deal with more than a very small fraction of the world, we will have to be transformed into something quite new and different, either through evolution or by our own intercession.

The Source of Human Behavior

While it may be accepted in principle that all aspects of life, including human mental processes, are reducible to physics and chemistry, there is no practical way of accounting for most specific human acts in these terms. Instead, it has been necessary to introduce the interpolating concepts of psychology, such as emotions, learning, personality, etc., and to use them to categorize human behavior. This may be thought of as the first step in a sequence, to be followed by a search for physiological mechanisms for the psychological functions. This search, which has already been successful in many cases, could then lead into a physical and chemical explanation of the physiological mechanisms, and so end in the reduction of mind to matter. Even if this could be accomplished, however, the purely psychological level of explanation would maintain its interest, since it provides much more direct intuitions and makes for easier communication about the connections between mental phenomena than any physical explanation possibly could.

Within the purely psychological approach, one of the important developments in the twentieth century has been the realization that many human character traits and motivations that had been thought to be innate or hereditary were instead learned behavior and very much tied to cultural influences. While there is some disagreement among psychologists on the precise degree of variability of specific motivations, such as the maternal drive or aggressiveness, it seems clear that the extent to which these operate does differ greatly between cultures. Furthermore, experiments both with animals and with humans have

shown that specific behavior patterns can be instilled by techniques such as conditioning or the
repetitive association of the desired behavior with
the satisfaction of some simple requirement such
as hunger. This was first demonstrated by Pavlov
in experiments with dogs and has become a
standard research tool for psychologists studying
animal behavior. For reasons that are partly
moral and partly practical, these techniques have
not been systematically used on human popula-
tions, except perhaps in the procedures known as
brainwashing. The psychologist B. F. Skinner
has, however, written a provocative utopian
novel, *Walden II,* outlining a society in which
such techniques are used to "engineer" human
behavior.[6]

To the extent that the human character is
malleable through conditioning or otherwise, an
inquiry into the goals of the human race must
consider whether it would be desirable to instill
some particular personality traits into all people.
It may be that a revision in man's psyche would
be more relevant to human happiness than any
transformation of the environment. In connection
with this possibility, important experiments have
been done in recent years on the influence of
electric stimuli and certain drugs on mental
states.[7] If we accept that mental phenomena involve physical and chemical transformations, it
is not surprising that these phenomena could be
altered by electrical impulses applied to the brain
from the outside, or by the administration of
drugs. Nevertheless, demonstrations that this

was the case, for example through the use of psychedelic drugs such as LSD, or through the control of animal behavior by external electrical signals, have had a certain shock effect and led to much extreme speculation on the potentialities of these techniques for good or evil.[8]

Certainly one must recognize that the discovery of any techniques for alteration of the personality, whether they use genetic, psychological, or physical methods, are a major development in our capabilities for self-determination. The method of manipulation would seem secondary to the aim being pursued. However, the possibility of such transformations of man has a dual role in the search for goals. It is both a tool for achieving some possible goals and a potentiality that we cannot decide whether or not to activate until we know our goals. For this reason, the question of transforming human personality from the outside will occur again and again in the following chapters.

SOME UNKNOWN FACTORS

A discussion of the implications of present science for human goals would be incomplete without some indication of the things we do not know that could be relevant to the goals we formulate. One may well ask whether there are not gaps in our knowledge of the world just as serious as those in the knowledge of ancient thinkers, which, I have argued, make their suggestions inappropriate for us. This problem may be considered on two levels. One is to grant that there may be serious gaps in our knowledge and to analyze the implications of this for goal making. This aspect of the problem is dealt with in Chapter V. The second approach, which I will discuss briefly here, is to examine the places where gaps in our knowledge could possibly exist and allow for these in our discussion of goals.

Are There Phenomena Inexplicable by Known Physical Laws?

The atomic theory of matter has provided explanations for almost all nonliving phenomena in nature. The outstanding exceptions to this are some problems concerning the properties of the components of atoms, the so-called elementary particles. The detailed properties of the elementary particles seem for the most part irrelevant to phenomena on any scale greater than atomic, however, and for that reason I think that what we do not know about particles is unlikely to affect our goals.[9]

There are, of course, many unsolved problems about nonliving phenomena in nature, and still more problems concerning living things. Scientists, however, believe that what is involved in the understanding of these things is not new physical laws or new entities, but rather a recognition of the implications of known laws in complex situations. This is in severe contrast to earlier times, when no general physical theory of natural phenomena was available, and there were a great number of everyday phenomena for which no explanation could be given even in principle. It therefore seems to me that the scientific questions relating to human goals that we cannot answer now deal mainly with technological possibilities, "Can such and such be done practically?" rather than with questions of fundamental science.

One important exception to this is the possible existence of psychic phenomena such as telepathy, which might be an exception to the conclusion that the known laws of physics are in principle capable of accounting for all mental activity, and which could indeed have important consequences for human goals if they existed. The evidence for psychic phenomena is not convincing to most scientists, although a number have said they believe that the reported experiments and observations do indicate that these phenomena exist.[10] Therefore, one open question to which an answer would be helpful in formulating human goals is whether there are people capable of telepathy, precognition, or the other activities known collectively as psychic phenomena.

Should the answer to this question be affirmative, we would then want to know how these phenomena fit in with other phenomena of physics, biology, and psychology. In particular, we would have to determine whether they are unexpected consequences of known laws. It would also be important to find out whether psychic abilities could be increased through training, or by some kind of artificial amplification. Some research has been attempted along these lines, without definitive results.[11] More work by objective scientists is clearly needed in this field.

What Is the Cause and Cure of Aging?

Another question to which no definite answer can as yet be given is whether aging and death are inevitable outcomes of human life. Although every known multicellular organism does age and eventually die, the cause and mechanism of aging is unknown. The usual analogy with the wearing out of a machine that is kept running is rather misleading, since living organisms are able to repair themselves continuously while machines cannot. Whether the individual cells comprising an organism age and lose their ability to grow and divide is not known. Nor is what determines the rate of aging in different organisms, causing the mayfly to die in a day while a man may live forty thousand times as long.

An understanding of how aging occurs could quite possibly lead to the ability to control or prevent it, and it is not easy to think of a discovery that would have greater implications for human life. Since we do not yet know whether or not this is possible, we must leave as open questions what the cause of aging is and whether the process can be prevented or controlled in human beings.

Some workers in this field have, however, estimated that answers to these questions will be forthcoming within the next twenty or thirty years.[12] I will therefore consider further in Chapter III some possible implications of an appreciable increase in the active human life span.

Is There Other Intelligent Life in the Universe?[13]

It is not yet proven but is considered quite likely by many scientists that planetary systems exist around many other stars. A few extrasolar planets have actually been detected, not by seeing them but through their gravitational effects. In view of the argument that living processes are merely complicated physiochemical changes and the theory that human life on earth is an evolution from inorganic beginnings through much simpler forms of life, it seems reasonable that life could have evolved on many of these other planets, although there is no evidence for this. If this has happened, we are naturally led to the conjecture that there may be other intelligent species besides man in the universe.

If intelligent extraterrestrial life is common, it is quite possible that some forms of life have progressed far beyond us, at least insofar as technology measures progress. The argument leading to this conclusion is based on the great age of the universe compared to the short history of man. Since evolution occurs to some extent through coincidences, there is no apparent reason why man, or something equivalent to him in intelligence, could not have appeared at a much earlier point in the history of a planet. If that should have happened elsewhere, then we might expect that such a species would be technologically advanced beyond us by some period comparable to the time difference between their emergence and ours, which could be hundreds of millions of years. In view of our own explosive technological growth in the last two hundred years, it is not unlikely that this lead time would mean that the accomplishments of the other species would be far in advance of our own. Although objections have been raised to the assumptions implicit in this reasoning, such as that intelligent life is very common in the universe, it seems on the whole a reasonable application of the Copernican principle that the earth does not have any preferred role in the universe.[14]

For the purpose of formulating human goals now we must consider the existence of other intelligent life an open question.

The discovery of extraterrestrial life, and especially intelligent life, would probably have profound consequences on the human outlook, and there have been proposals that we undertake a systematic search for evidence of such life by various means.[15] Such a search will come well within our technical abilities in the next few centuries, and I will consider its implications briefly in the next chapter.

There are other unsolved scientific problems relevant to human goals, but, like the questions given above, they are fairly definite questions to which we can begin looking for answers, rather than mysteries that we cannot attack. Therefore, while there may be surprises in store for us, everything we know indicates that our general scientific picture of the world can serve as a reasonably accurate map to help us choose where we want to go. Other factors, which I will discuss later, may place more severe restrictions on how well we can do this.

THE HUMAN CONDITION

In all choices of goals, either personal or group, certain attitudes toward human life as it is currently lived, or what I will call the human condition, are implicit. For some the attitude is disgust or despair at man's poor lot.[16] For others it is a celebration of the splendor of man's life and expectations.[17] For still others, it is quiet resignation in the face of irresistible and inimical force.[18] Given such a spectrum of opinions, we can hardly expect to come to any general consensus about the human condition in the late twentieth century. Nevertheless I intend to take up this question, partly so that the reader can see what my own presuppositions are, and partly because of the new possibilities open to us for changing human nature. Through the latter possibilities even those holding the most pessimistic attitudes may be convinced that we are not eternally damned.

In discussing the human condition, I will consider the most favorable external circumstances. That is, I will take as examples the relatively well-to-do members of advanced societies, who are not burdened by any abnormal physical or mental defects. Admittedly, this excludes a large majority of the human race. I have, however, already noted that I expect these conditions to be shared by most human beings in the relatively near future, i.e., the twenty-first century. Also, I believe that the similarities in our condition are more profound than the differences in culture, living standards, and health would suggest.

What characterizes the human condition for these relatively favored individuals? That it is easier to express the negative aspects than the positive indicates perhaps that we are subconsciously comparing what is with some ideal of what might be. The most serious fault in the human condition lies in our finitude. We are conscious beings aware of our own limitations. Two of the most important of these are the lack of power to do things we want to do, and the specter of impending death, which always threatens to put an end to all our thinking and doing.

Wanting to Do More Than We Can

Probably the first stage in an infant's realization of the separation between himself and everything outside is the discovery that there are aspects of the world not subject to his will. But even after this primary division, the most fundamental of all the mind's categorizations, is made, the mature individual generally does not reach an equilibrium with his environment. That is to say, we do not usually desire exactly those things we will be able to achieve, but rather something more. The fulfillment of a given desire is usually the signal for some new wish rather than a cause for contentment. This behavior is recognized by writers in a wide variety of cultures, although their attitudes toward it vary from Browning's commendatory couplet[19]

> *A man's reach should exceed his grasp*
> *Or what's a heaven for!*

to the Buddha's characterization of such "selfish craving" as the true cause of unhappiness, which is to be avoided by following the Eightfold Way.[20]

The extent to which man's desires exceed his abilities varies between individuals and especially between different cultures. It seems particularly strong in Faustian cultures such as the contemporary Western world and relatively weak in Apollonian groups such as the Zuñi Indians.[21] But I think that these differences are only comparative and that to an important extent all men suffer from this aspect of being finite creatures.

Men have proposed two sorts of solutions to the problem of wanting more than they can get. One, the renunciation of the desire, is the approach of the Buddhists and certain other groups, such as the Stoics. Roughly speaking, the point of Buddhist renunciation is that our desires are at fault and that whether or not they can be satisfied, we will be better off if they are curbed. The main problem here is that if we live in the world and have the typical human heredity and upbringing, there are constant temptations that provoke the unwanted desires in us. Therefore, Buddhism tends to lead to a renunciation not only of desire, but also of the world that calls it forth. Many people who are troubled by the gap between desire and fulfillment are unwilling to pay that price for eliminating it.

Another solution to the disparity between will and achievement, which appears more natural to most people in the Western world, particularly to Americans, is to regard as only temporary any inability to accomplish something we want to do or to fulfill any desire. If we are convinced that the future will see our wishes come true, we may not be so unhappy about the fact that they cannot be immediately satisfied. In fact, for some who practice this philosophy, the anticipation of future satisfaction may become more important than the satisfaction itself.

It might be possible to indoctrinate almost everyone with this attitude through suitable training and so ameliorate one of the tragedies of being finite. To some extent, this approach has been one of America's contributions to the human outlook. Those who have been so indoctrinated are, however, particularly vulnerable to another aspect of our finitude, the fact that our lives are limited by age and death. It is difficult to maintain the belief that all our dreams will eventually come true when we are weakened by age or when we sense death approaching, either for ourselves or for others who are important to us. Therefore, if one adopts the attitude of "there's always tomorrow," for the solution of the problem of yet unfulfilled wishes, one must then decide on what attitude to take toward death.

The Shadow of Death

Since this problem also exists for those with other attitudes toward unfulfilled wishes, it must really be considered in its own terms. Unless and until the steps toward indefinite life and youth to be discussed in Chapter III prove successful, we must all face the certainty of our own deaths and the deaths of those we care about. Even to those who sincerely believe in a life after death, the discontinuity involved is so great that it is difficult to think of death as we think of the different events in life. Again, a number of attitudes have been adopted by different men. Some have felt that death, at least among the aged, is to be regarded as a relief from the weariness of long life.[22] Others have called it the Last Enemy, which mankind will have to deal with even after all its other problems are solved.[23] Such men, who do not welcome death, have to adopt some point of view about how to deal with it when it arrives, either for themselves or for friends and relatives.

In choosing a point of view, a man implicitly decides what it is about death that is bad for him. For Epicurus, personal death was not to be feared because after death one no longer exists, and nothing bad can happen to the nonexistent. This attitude can be a great source of strength to someone who is really convinced of it. But it has two drawbacks. One is that nothing good can happen to the nonexistent either, and to the extent that we obtain present joy from anticipation of the future, the possibility that death will annul our plans is an obstacle to this joy. It is not, to be sure, unique in this respect; other things frequently interfere with future plans. The other drawback of the Epicurean attitude to death is that it is not relevant to our grief over the death of another person, which is the major part of the problem for the living.

The Buddhists have suggested a solution to this aspect of death by telling us not to become emotionally involved with the transitory things of this world, such as other human beings, so that we will not suffer when they pass away. This injunction to "care less" about one another does not seem to strike a chord in most people, although some are naturally responsive to it. Again, it is probable that it could be systematically instilled into people through psychological training, but the effects of such an attitude on human relationships would probably be such as to make this choice undesired by most people.

Probably the most prevalent attitude toward death among naturalistic thinkers is one of quiet resignation in the face of a situation that cannot be avoided; Socrates and Hume are ideal illustrations. Some commentators have held that this is what we should all aspire to, and have sometimes gone even further and argued that the fight against death being pursued by science and medicine is wrong because it is not sufficiently in harmony with the spirit of resignation. Such a view is again unlikely to be attractive to most men, who seem to agree intuitively that death should be opposed as far as possible.

To those who accept this view, the possibility of the indefinite postponement of death that may soon come about through advances in biology will be most welcome. Perhaps the only true solution to the problem of death is to eliminate it for those who do not desire it. Only then will man have a free choice in the matter.

But even "at death's end" men will remain finite beings in their accomplishments if not in their expectations. I do not know whether the opportunity to exercise our abilities over an indefinite time period will itself be an answer to the unhappiness over our finitude. We will have to wait to see. If this should not prove the case, then some other kind of reconstruction of man appears called for to deal with finitude.

The Meaning of Life

Another flaw in the human condition as it exists today is the feeling among so many people that their lives are meaningless. Some writers have assumed that this problem is peculiar to the contemporary Western world, as a result of the loss of religious faith and the weakening of family ties. In my opinion, this is a misleading assumption. One need only look into Ecclesiastes to realize that our age has no monopoly on the feeling that life is meaningless. Furthermore, if it is because of a change in social institutions that people's lives lack a meaning, then this meaning cannot be an intrinsic thing, and one can imagine other institutions that might supply different, but equally satisfying meanings for the lives of those raised under them. To some extent, this occurs in microsocieties like the Israeli kibbutz or the Chinese commune.

When someone says that his life has no meaning or that life in general is meaningless, one thing he is saying is that there is nothing outside himself that offers valid guidance in making decisions about how to act or in what activities to spend his life. Such statements also often indicate unhappiness about the insignificance of man in comparison to the natural world, and state that this insignificance is part of the reason for feeling that life is meaningless. This attitude has certainly been accentuated by the scientific discoveries of the past few centuries, particularly the recognition of the continuity of man with the rest of nature and the realization of the immense scale of the universe. Perhaps in this sense it is fair to say that the problem of a lack of meaning to life is more severe in our time than it has been in the past.

Men's reactions to the lack of an external standard for making choices are varied. Existentialists like Sartre, far from deploring this situation, celebrate as the core of man's humanity the fact that he himself must make choices.[24] A contrary view is taken by such writers as Dostoevski, who apparently felt that in the absence of religious faith, man's naturally base instincts would lead him into savagery.[25] Both of these views implicitly assume that man's behavior and thought are intrinsic rather than determined by his upbringing and environment.

One can, like the Marxists and many psychologists, make the alternative assumption that man's mind is a blank slate on which the pattern is drawn by his life.[26] Then one may be led to the conclusion that a sense of purpose to life must be provided by society, or by whoever is forming the man's general outlook. From this standpoint, men who claim that their lives have no meaning have missed something in their training, just as if they had not been taught to write.

To this it might be retorted that the question is not whether a man can be made to feel a sense of purpose or meaning in his life by certain ways of upbringing, but whether the meaning he is convinced of is a delusion, which was enforced on him by equally deluded adults when he had not the wit to resist them, and which he can no longer rid himself of. Such a view seems to me close to that expressed by Freud in *Civilization and Its Discontents*.[27] It applies most specifically as a description of those people whom David Riesman has called "inner-directed,"[28] although Riesman would not accept the pejorative view that inner direction involves a delusion on the part of the inner-directed.

The idea that any view that one's life has a specific meaning or purpose is a delusion seems unwarranted. A delusion involves some contradiction between a belief that is held and the objective truth. If we agree that there is no external standard that defines such a purpose, then there is no possibility that any purpose taken by an individual to motivate his life can be in conflict with the truth. The most one could say is that such a choice is an arbitrary one for which there is no objective warrant. This criticism can, however, be made of every belief a man has that does not deal with matters of fact. If there is no intellectual stigma attached to holding ethical or esthetic beliefs even if they cannot be objectively justified, then there seems to be no reason for deprecating those who by one method or another have become convinced that their life has a purpose.

If one feels that the lack of a purpose in a man's life is a misfortune, then one may sympathize with efforts to provide such a purpose in the lives of others who may be still open to such conviction. In this connection, if we are successful in formulating goals for the human race, it may be easier for some people to find a purpose in their own lives. Once long-term goals have been formulated, many people who grow up in the society that has accepted these goals will find it natural to choose the furthering of them as the main purpose of their individual lives. This kind of choice has been made so often by people in more restricted groups, such as religious or political sects, that I would confidently predict that it will happen again with the goals of the human race.

I have emphasized the two problems of human finitude and the meaning of individual lives because I think they are the deepest troubles with the human condition as it is in the best of present circumstances. There are, of course, other problems that are much more immediate for many people. Much of the world often does not have simple subsistence. Even among people with high living standards, there is the problem of interpersonal relations, which to many men has seemed the most difficult of human problems. I have not dwelt on these because I think that they are less fundamental in that, since solutions exist for them already in some cases, we can optimistically hope that in the course of time they will be solved universally. For the two problems I have considered, the solution may require more radical steps.

Human Goals and the Human Condition

In spite of all its faults, the human condition is not entirely one of desperation. Life also holds for many of us the joys of achievement and of anticipation, of contemplation and of spontaneous action, of gratifying our own desires and of giving pleasure to others. And we bear the proud and lonely distinction of being the only known part of the world that has self-awareness.

It is not possible to make any truly objective

statements about the good and bad things in human life. Any individual's list probably reveals more about the psychology of that individual than it does about humanity. But a consensus among the human race about what is good and bad in the human condition would serve to *define* these terms and perhaps indicate something about the direction we might take in modifying man.

Depending upon how one weighs the balance of good and bad things in human life, one would probably think it necessary to have more or less radical changes in human beings in order to produce a more ideal state. My own feeling is that the despair of the conscious mind at the recognition of its own finitude is such that man cannot achieve an abiding contentment in his present form or anything like it. Therefore, I believe that a transformation of man into something very different from what he is now is called for. But I do not know to what extent my fellow men will agree with me here.

There is one other reservation I should express here about the accuracy of these judgments. Even the most advantaged of men in our culture grow up under severe burdens of various sorts. Some of these could certainly be lifted by the kind of piecemeal reform that most social thinkers are concerned with—I have in mind such things as not repressing the natural curiosity of children. Perhaps when man is freed from these removable burdens, he will be able to find himself, in ways that are not obvious to us who still carry them.

This has been the hope of many reformers of the social system throughout history. The fact that it has not so far turned out that way is not necessarily a proof that these methods will never work. But I think that those of us who find the human condition basically unsatisfactory must seek other methods as well.

The most radical proposals along these lines would be that man should reconstruct his biological and psychological nature so that the present faults in his condition are corrected. If this road is chosen, it means that we will have accepted the fact that not only is nonhuman nature subject to man's will in how it is to function, but that man has the choice of what he himself is to be. Such an attitude is perhaps a logical extension of setting goals for humanity. The two are not synonymous because some goals could be set within the framework of what man is, accepting this as part of the rules. In my opinion, we should not wish to be bound by this restriction, once we recognize that the modification of man is open to us through the understanding of our biology and our psychology. This is, however, a matter upon which honorable men may differ, and perhaps it will be the subject of one of the "Great Debates" of the twenty-first century.

Those who accept the possibility of reconstructing man can avoid some of the despair that many have felt over man's fate. This involves a certain amount of altruism, because it is probably not we the living who will benefit from the reconstruction, but rather those yet to be born, or at least yet to be shaped. It seems to me fairly clear that most men have at least enough altruism to wish to save others from a misery that they themselves are suffering. The belief that "tomorrow will be better," at least for their children, has helped many men suffer today's ills more cheerfully, and the same would probably hold true after a decision to reconstruct man so as to eliminate the faults in his life. Although this is only a fringe benefit of the decision, it is perhaps all that will accrue to those making it, and therefore it should not be dismissed lightly.

I do not, however, think that the goals of humanity should be wholly or even primarily determined by the desire to fix the flaws in the human condition, even insofar as these flaws are a matter of consensus. There is much of worth in what we are, and goals that are an expression of these positive features in man are at least as important as the others. Unfortunately, most utopian schemes have concentrated on eliminating the negative, rather than accentuating the positive. Hence more thought will be required in this direction. I see no reason to doubt that proposals along these lines will be forthcoming.

All those who have proposed goals for the human race in the past have made their own assumptions, explicitly or otherwise, about the human condition. In the analysis of some of these goals to be presented in Chapter IV, I will try to make these assumptions explicit and also indicate where I disagree with them. As in the case of the choice of goals itself, I think that a decision on what is good or bad about human life is a matter of feeling rather than of understanding. For that reason I am content to leave the decision to the same court, that is, to the judgment of humanity itself.

III. Some Roads That Will Be Opened

In the next fifty years it is possible that, for the first time, decisions will be consciously made whose consequences will radically transform human life. Radical transformations have, of course, occurred before in history, for example with the discovery of agriculture, and again with the Industrial Revolution. What is new this time is that the changes may occur as the result of decisions based on a rational analysis of what the desired goal is, together with some understanding of the probable consequences of action.

In the Agricultural and Industrial Revolutions, the transformations took place over quite long periods and involved a number of minor, more or less independent steps. There was little knowledge on the part of the innovators or the societies adopting the innovations of what the long-range effects would be.[1] It is likely that a sizable fraction of the inhabitants of pre-industrial Europe or of the pre-agricultural neolithic tribes would have strenuously resisted the innovations had they known of their eventual consequences. (The Luddites, who did resist industrialization, were motivated by more personal considerations, such as the loss of their livelihoods.) We, their descendants, are usually happy that this did not occur.

The present situation has several qualitatively new features that make it more desirable and probably also more feasible to calculate the effects of a decision. There is first of all the contracted time scale over which the changes could take place. While the Agricultural Revolution took several millennia and the Industrial Revolution several centuries to develop, the results of the decisions I will discuss may come about much more rapidly, because of the interdependence of different parts of the modern world and the greater magnitude of the forces controlled by contemporary technology. As a result of these factors, we should expect that the time scale for major changes in human civilization will soon be about one generation. The time people require to learn new things might limit any more rapid change, although this mental ability may be improvable artificially, and there is also, as we shall see, the possibility of intelligent nonhuman influences, which might shorten the time scale even further.

If our lives may be transformed so rapidly that the world in which a man is educated to live no longer exists when he is an adult, then some analysis is called for of what changes will occur as a result of some step. The same factors that lead to a shortening of the time scale also tend to make such analysis easier. Thus the advance of technology means that more of the factors entering into any change are under human control, and hence more easily calculable, than in earlier times, when uncontrollable natural causes played a more important role. Also, the technical unity of the world that is developing implies a greater homogeneity of conditions, which should make it easier to estimate the effects of a decision.

Another feature of some present and future decisions that is relevant here is their "irreversible" character. That is, as a result of some decision, the human way of life may change so drastically that there is no realistic possibility of returning to the previous way. Furthermore, this change may foreclose forever a whole range of options that men might otherwise have followed. This irreversibility comes from several sources. One is the trend toward homogeneity of the human race. Because all human societies are becoming similar, it is unlikely that any islands of humanity could remain untouched by changes put into effect by the rest of the world. This trend is sure to increase as communication improves and the recognition of the unity of mankind becomes more widespread. Hence any sweeping change in man is likely to become worldwide; there will be no reservoir of unchanged men to follow alternative possibilities, unless we consciously choose to maintain such a reservoir.

Another source of irreversibility is the changes in the most fundamental aspects of human existence, such as man's biology, or his psychology, that the decisions may involve. As we shall see in some specific instances, such changes necessarily intensify certain aspects of human life at the expense of others. In the new situation that will then be created, some new possibilities will exist, but some old ones will vanish. We can make an analogy with a traveler at a fork in a road where there are many routes. Although he can follow any one route, he cannot take them all, and taking one precludes following any of the others. Furthermore, if he follows one branch for very long, it may be difficult or impossible to retrace his steps later, and the different branches may lead to very different destinations. This situation is aptly described by Robert Frost in his poem, "The Road Not Taken." To be sure, all choices involve the elimination of some possibilities, but when we are considering fundamental changes in man, the possibilities that we are ruling out by the change may be very substantial ones, and we had better know the consequences of what we are doing.

Somewhat paradoxically, it may be easier to determine these consequences for "world-shaking decisions" than for less important ones. In the former case some of the consequences are so important that we can concentrate on the factors determining these and neglect other incidental results. Hence it seems possible to determine in advance when some action may have irreversible effects and, at least in broad outline, what these effects would be.

In such cases we can take advantage of developments in the social sciences. It is not just temporal chauvinism that makes one feel that we are better armed than any period in the past with methods for analyzing complicated intellectual problems. For one thing, there is a larger number of people working on such problems. For another, the cumulative character of human intellectual effort makes an insight that was achieved only with difficulty in one generation the working tool of the next. Finally—and this will be of more importance in the future—we have developed computers that can perform some operations not possible to humans because of the time and accuracy required. Therefore, while it cannot yet be claimed that the social sciences can make accurate predictions in very complicated situations, we are much better off in this respect than previous cultures have been.

The questions that immediately arise are, who should make these "world-shaking decisions," and on what basis should they be made? A common characteristic of all the crucial decisions that may arise from the progress of science is that their consequences will last for a long time, and affect many people. Therefore, they should be made on the basis of fundamental principles, taking these long-term effects into account. Ordinarily, decisions are not made on such a basis in our society or any other, with the possible exception of some religious institutions. Political institutions, particularly in the democratic countries, have been designed so that it is difficult for one government administration to commit its successors very firmly to any course of action. This has worked as a built-in safety factor against temporary excesses of zeal and has often served a useful purpose in this way. It has also, however, tended to discourage governments from thinking about problems that have a longer time scale than one or two decades. The Soviet government has a better record in this respect, probably because of its positive attitude toward social planning in general.

I think it unlikely that the organs of government will have spontaneously changed enough by the time of the world-shaking decisions to be sufficiently sensitive to the long-term issues involved. Furthermore, in the process of governmental decision-making there are inescapable elements of such immediate concern as getting elected, which tends to blur matters of principle. It would therefore be unwise to leave the initiative of deciding about the technological possibilities to the workings of governments, even though these are the natural institutions through which society will react to these possibilities.

I think it would also be unwise to leave such decisions to the scientists who originate the technical innovations, as has sometimes been suggested. Scientists are too selective a group to encompass the variety of interests and yearnings displayed by mankind as a whole; their decisions are unlikely to be based on all of the factors relevant to something that will affect so many people so profoundly. The other side of this coin is that scientists, particularly those engaged in a particular piece of research, are likely to put a high premium on completing that research without too much concern over whatever social consequences it may eventually produce. This is not meant as a negative moral judgment, but rather as an empirical observation.

Finally, I think that the suggestion of leaving such decisions to the scientists misses the point that such decisions require a consensus on goals, which does not yet exist. Scientists are trained to discover facts, not to reach an ethical consensus. It is therefore a misconception of their function, as well as a misunderstanding of the relation between matters of ethics and matters of fact to place on the scientists a burden that belongs to all of us.

A better approach to the problem of making world-shaking decisions would be for various groups, with as wide a composition as possible, to discuss these problems. If such a discussion is carried through on a broad enough scale, it can create a climate of understanding of what we want in which government action can be relatively automatic, without requiring much of the systematic analysis for which government institutions are ill-suited. Under these circumstances, which I hope might be an outgrowth of the Prometheus Project, the government might really serve the "general will of the people" in making these decisions.

If something like this does not happen, it seems probable that decisions with very great consequences will be made on grounds of simple expediency, either by whoever first becomes capable of carrying through some development, or by some government body that has neither the will nor the capability to see the long-term effects of the decision. If we wish to avoid this, an ethical framework must be provided for the analysis of long-term effects. After this is done, a "calculus" of important decisions will become as feasible as it is necessary. Let us then examine some examples of decisions that we will soon have to face, and we will see that without a new ethical basis, rational decisions will be impossible.

In the last few years there has been a substantial increase of interest in the prediction of future developments in technology.[2] These predictions have ranged from individual leaps of imagination in restricted fields to systematic efforts by teams of experts in many disciplines to make general predictions of what technology will and will not have accomplished by a given time, often the year 2000. These attempts at prophecy are quite interesting, but I do not think we can rely on them even for setting the limits of what we can expect technology to accomplish.

In general, past attempts to predict the future development of technology over any long period have been rather unsuccessful.[3] Most of them, even those made by scientists, have erred on the side of pessimism rather than optimism. One may guess that the reason for this is that the daily work of scientists requires a careful distinction between what is known and what is unknown, whereas successful conjectures about future advances often involve speculation about what may be accomplished by methods as yet unknown.

For that reason, predictions by science fiction writers, who are more willing to speculate, perhaps because they have less to lose professionally by doing so, have generally been better at anticipating really spectacular advances in technology than those by scientists.

Because of the difficulty of making accurate predictions, I will not try to give an exhaustive list of what possibilities will be opened by technology in, say, the next five hundred years. Instead, I will discuss a few technical advances that have been proposed by working scientists as not going very far beyond what is now known, and that I expect may therefore come about within the next century. We shall see that if any one of these developments occurs, it will give us a good deal to think about concerning long-range goals, and the situation will be intensified if more than one occurs.

BIOLOGICAL ENGINEERING[4]

By biological engineering, I mean the design and manipulation of biological organisms, including human beings, so that certain of their functions can be better performed. Some types of biological engineering, such as selective breeding of plants and animals for particular traits or the administration of drugs for the cure of diseases, such as diabetes, in which the organism cannot produce some vital substance, have been carried out extensively in the past. However, these methods produce relatively superficial changes in comparison to those made by physical engineering in inorganic systems.

As our knowledge of the workings of biological systems increases, we can expect to be able to control their functions more profoundly. In particular, the recognition of the central role of large molecules such as DNA in heredity suggests the possibility of making substitutions in or additions to the genetic content of cells, with a consequent change in the biological function.[5] Such an alteration would be qualitatively different from either selective breeding or administration of drugs. This type of genetic engineering could, for example, be applied to the somatic cells that make up the body, rather than to just the germ cells. In this case, the alterations would affect the life process of the individual on which they were made, rather than, as is the case with selective breeding, affecting only his descendants. Furthermore, the altered individual would be in some aspects a new individual, since after the DNA is changed, it continues to replicate itself in the altered condition, and therefore the change in the function of the cells will continue for the life of the individual. This is in contrast to the use of a drug, where the function returns to its original form when the drug is stopped. Thus in the case of a diabetes victim, genetic manipulation could be used to change the pancreatic cells from their defective form in which insulin is not produced, to the normal form in which it is produced, after which the individual could live normally, without the need for externally supplied insulin. This type of biological engineering might be thought of as analogous to replacing a defective part of a machine by a new part.

Another form of biological engineering can be imagined that would be more analogous to replacing one machine or part of a machine by a more efficient one. It is clear that there are some biological activities that are not performed as effectively as we would like and others that we cannot do at all. For example, the body's capacity for self-repair is rather limited, particularly in the central nervous system. Mental functions, too, are not optimal in humans as now constructed, and it is possible to imagine that men could be much more intelligent than any yet born. It does not seem unreasonable that a redesign of some aspects of the workings of bodies and brains could remedy these deficiencies and produce beings differing from present man in respects that many people would consider desirable. One could imagine that even here it would be possible to do this with already existing people, preserving that part of their personality that makes them unique. This, however, may be difficult.

A further stage of biological engineering would be the design of new individuals for whom the new abilities would be a part from the beginning of their life. Such individuals might be made by the production of a modified form of DNA, which would contain genetic information to encode the formation of cells, etc., with the new functions desired. Obviously, in view of the complicated interactions between different parts of a biological system, a great deal of new knowledge will be required to make this feasible, although there seems to be no reason why it could not be done.

The techniques by which such biological engineering could be accomplished are not yet available, but we appear to be on the road to developing them. It should be understood that more is involved here than a detailed understanding of the properties of DNA molecules. In order to construct an organism that will perform some particular function such as regeneration of damaged organs, it is necessary to know the gross physiological mechanisms by which the function will be done, as well as the proper molecular arrangements in the genes to guarantee that these physiological mechanisms will be produced in the organism. Thus biological engineering will require progress in the classical areas of biology as well as in the newer molecular biology. It is like the construction of a nuclear submarine, which required both the discovery of the subatomic phenomena of nuclear fission and advances in such large-scale engineering techniques as heat exchange and propulsion. We need a biological systems engineering of the kind developed for dealing with complicated inorganic systems, which involve many components and many different steps in order to reach a definite end, such as manned flight to the moon. In inorganic systems engineering the use of high-speed computers has played a decisive role, since what is involved is not so much creative thought as the analysis of a great number of possibilities. We may expect that the computers of the future will play an equally decisive role in the design of the men of the future.

If the reader has been convinced by these admittedly sketchy arguments that it will soon be possible to remold man, he will almost certainly be asking the obvious question of what changes would be desirable. Indeed, this is the crucial question for a still more general circumstance. The fact that "the nature of man" is plastic under a variety of forces, including biological engineering, psychological conditioning, etc., urgently raises the question of what forms of man are to be preferred and condoned.

In the early stages of biological engineering, as already mentioned, the techniques will probably be used to correct obvious flaws, including genetically caused diseases such as diabetes, and certain forms of hereditary feeble-mindedness. In this stage, the genetic manipulations will have the effect of removing some of the disadvantages people have because of the different chromosomes of their ancestors and, at least with regard to the elimination of unfavorable traits, will tend to make everyone approach the levels of the best-endowed normal men. It is unlikely that many moral objections will be raised against such forms of manipulation, especially since genetic engineering, when developed, will vitiate some of the complaints that have occasionally been heard to the effect that medical progress is keeping alive some people who carry unfavorable genes. It must be noted, however, that even this type of engineered uniformity could have important social consequences. For instance, physical beauty in either sex may well be one of the traits amenable to such manipulation. It would take a braver man than I to estimate the effects on our culture of the possibility of choosing one's physical appearance at will, within the limitations of age. Although the problems posed by corrective biological engineering are interesting, they are peripheral to the major concerns of this book, which are raised more directly by biological redesign.

As long as the manipulations of the biological engineers are restricted to enabling some men to overcome the shortcomings of their heredity and meet the prevailing human norms there is not much question of choice involved. Once, however, it becomes possible to go beyond anything that has existed before among men, the problem of choice becomes immediate. The problem will be particularly acute in the second state of biological engineering, when it may be possible to induce certain traits only at the expense of others. For example, it might be possible to make the human memory much more reliable and consciously accessible at the expense of a decrease in the breadth of our sensory responses. There are two types of choices involved in such situations. One is the choice of the individual as to whether he wishes such a change to be carried out on himself or on his children. The other is the choice of society as to whether it should allow the willful creation of this new form of man.

Few people would be likely to defend the view that no improvements are possible in the biological functioning of men. On the other hand, any particular suggestion of modifications has a good chance of meeting with resistance from some part of the population. If men could be made who were appreciably more intelligent than anyone is at present, some people would object on the grounds that this would aggravate the estrangement of man from a preferable, uncontemplative state. A breed of man that would live much longer than we do would be opposed, perhaps by many, on the grounds that age and death are a natural development from life.[6]

In view of the likelihood of such disagreements on standards for what changes in man are desirable, the simplest solution might seem to be a laissez-faire system in which society took no position on this at all. For several reasons, I believe this would be a very dangerous course to take. It would almost certainly lead to an immense proliferation of types of man, differing in much more substantial ways than the present races do. This would have the effect of undoing the slow growth of unity in mankind described earlier. While there are undoubtedly merits in a diversity of human potential and function, one need only recognize the difficulties caused by the existing minor variations in man to realize that an uncontrolled increase in human variability would make a viable society much more difficult, and perhaps impossible, to achieve, at least in the foreseeable future.

Another reason why some sort of control by society over biological engineering is important is the basically altruistic feeling that society should guarantee to all individuals, particularly children, equal access to the best opportunities the world has to offer, independent of the wishes of their parents, relations, etc. This motive, which lies behind free public education, enforced medical care, etc., implies the principle that society at large has the responsibility to ensure that its members do not suffer from evitable disadvantages in their lives. As a consequence of this, if a major fraction of society decided, for example, that they or their children should achieve greatly increased longevity through biological engineering, there probably would be strong social pressure to make such longevity universal, even for the children of those who did not consider it a good thing. At least this seems like a reasonable extension of adding fluorides to the water supply to reduce dental cavities.

Since society is likely to require some controls over modifications of man, it is important to recognize that such controls, particularly if they take the form of enforcing certain changes thought to be desirable, could result in a substantial transformation of human life. Suppose it were decided that children to be born in the future should be biologically modified so that their mental powers were greatly increased in such respects as much better memories, faster thought processes, ability to concentrate on a number of problems simultaneously, or any of the other mental abilities that men have wished for. It is likely that the intelligent children, once grown to maturity, would be somewhat impatient with a society designed for their more dull-witted ancestors and would set about changing it to fit their own needs. Descriptions of the type of conflict that might ensue have been given in a number of science fiction stories.[7] Such a confrontation between man and superman may be an extreme example of the consequences of biological engineering. Nevertheless, it does point to what I think is a common factor among the consequences of the different modifications that might be made: when man, rather than the environment, is being modified, the results are no longer under the control of the modifier but are individuals with their own wills and motivations. Hence, one cannot necessarily undo what has been done without arbitrary interference in human lives. While such interference may be intolerable after the fact, it is hard to see any moral objection to trying to avoid such conflicts by prior analysis of what a particular modification might lead to.

This suggests that efforts to control biological modification of man will have to be carefully thought out in advance, not only in their technical aspects, but, more significantly, in their ethical aspects, and many of the biologists involved in the research that will lead to biological engineering have called for just such thought.[8]

There does not seem to be any escape from the conclusion that some agreement is necessary among the members of society as to what modifications should be encouraged and allowed. Such agreement is not likely to be easily attained in any large group because of the diverse individual ideals of the members. It is at this point that some consensus on the ultimate goals of mankind could aid in reaching agreement on such a concrete issue.

To see how this might work, let us suppose that it was agreed that a goal for the human race was for each of its members to achieve the kind of insight into himself and the universe that mystics have always extolled as the truest form of knowledge.[9] That is to say, every man should be able to reach what the Zen Buddhists call satori, or Enlightenment. A more detailed analysis of this type of goal will be given later on. If it were adopted, several consequences would seem to follow for the kinds of biological manipulations to be encouraged. Modifications of man that put more of his biological functions under conscious control would be considered good from this point of view, as would be changes in the workings of his mind that resulted in more of a conscious and less of an unconscious mind. Conversely, changes in human biology that resulted in a greater dependence on stimuli outside the individual for pleasure or for instruction would be discouraged. More generally, it is obvious that if the attainment of mystic enlightenment is the goal, and if we understand any of the perquisites of such enlightenment, then biological engineering can be used to produce men more capable of it. Since mystics have not been averse to using biological methods, such as deep breathing, in the past in their quest for enlightenment, this type of artificial aid cannot be immediately dismissed as overly materialistic.

The principle involved here is more general, of course. Many human goals will involve some transformation of man as well as a transformation of his environment. Biological engineering is one method by which such transformations of man can be carried out, and in some respects it is the most direct. Therefore, if there was agreement on goals, it is probable that some very specific types of biological transformations of man would be called for in order to help carry them out. And other transformations that would be antagonistic to the goals could be resisted on that basis.

If mankind is transformed through conscious biological manipulation, the new men that are produced will have a different set of interests and potentialities than we do. In making this change, we will therefore have started on a road that could not easily be retraced, not because the biological manipulation could not be undone, but because the new man is not likely to wish to reintroduce the attributes of contemporary man in himself. Therefore, to some extent, this kind of change in man will involve a renunciation of certain possibilities that now exist for the human race. In principle this might be avoided by allowing the change to be carried out on only a fraction of humanity, but this would probably not be feasible if the change seems very desirable. Hence biological engineering is likely to lead to some of the irreversible changes we have discussed. It is therefore incumbent on us to consider the merits of some of the possibilities that will be closed by carrying out a particular change, in comparison to some that will be opened up by it. This again requires some consensus on long-range goals if we are to avoid purely opportunistic solutions to the problem.

Thus the acceptance of goals for humanity could provide both positive and negative guidelines for the control of biological engineering by society. The extent to which such controls should be imposed is a more subtle question, which I touch upon in Chapter V, since it involves, among other matters, the question of how an agreed-upon goal should affect the life of an individual. I would like to remark at this point that I can sympathize with a view that too much interference with individual freedom is involved in the kind of controls over biological engineering by society that I have discussed. If we wish to avoid the interference involved, it may be necessary to renounce the modification of man through biological engineering altogether, which does not seem a likely development to me. Therefore, I think that the need for this kind of control is implicit in the possibility of biological engineering, and we had best think about the general principles that will determine what controls to impose.

ARTIFICIAL INTELLIGENCE

For our second case study in future technology, let us consider the possibility of constructing intelligent or superintelligent machines. In the past twenty-five years, the capabilities of electronic computers for carrying out operations that could previously be done only by human beings has increased tremendously. Although the first applications of computers were to problems in mathematics and science, they now play an important role in other scholarly work, as well as in many commercial activities. Experimental work has been done toward developing computers that can perform more creative activities such as writing music, proving mathematical theorems, and recognizing patterns.[10]

A certain amount of controversy has been generated about how far electromechanical machines can be developed in the direction of duplicating and perhaps surpassing human mental functions. Some commentators are not convinced that the present accomplishments of computers imply that the computer thinks, or ever will be able to think.[11] These writers point out that present computers perform simple operations such as counting very rapidly and so are able to solve problems that humans have reduced to the repetition of such simple operations. However, they argue, there is no reason to believe that the computers operate in any fashion similar to the way the human brain operates, or that such operation can be duplicated in the near future, particularly since it is not understood in any detail how the brain does work.

Other writers, including some who are working on such problems, are convinced that machines that duplicate human intellectual functions are not far off.[12] In this connection, it is important to recognize that a machine may be able to do something the human brain does by a quite different method. If one defines intelligence functionally, in terms of what results are produced rather than how the organism produces them, it becomes clear that our failure to understand how the human mind works is not necessarily a bar to producing intelligent machines. This distinction is also relevant to the question of communication with hypothetical intelligent extraterrestrial beings, who also may not have brains that work in the same way as ours.

As a functional definition of intelligence, let us call a system intelligent if it is able to provide, on demand, the answer to certain kinds of questions. The questions involved may be abstract, such as, "What is the density of the material obtained by combining sodium and chlorine?" or practical, such as, "Which of the following stocks will increase most in price within the next six months?" The machine may answer by consulting a large memory, or by combining elements of its memory through logical operations, or by some process different from anything used by humans. The process by which the machine comes to its answer seems to me irrelevant to the question of its intelligence. After all, different human beings may use different methods to find the answers to questions, and we are still prepared to use the term intelligence for their different activities. If one gives a test to a group of students, some may remember the answers to the questions from lectures or readings, while others, who do not, will work out the answers from other things they know. While admitting that there is a difference between these activities, one does not hesitate to grade the students on the results, i.e., the answers to the problems, however they are obtained.

If the method by which a machine is able to answer questions is not decisive in determining its intelligence, still less is the often-advanced agreement that the machine was built, or programmed, by a human being. This is analogous to saying that a man cannot be intelligent because he is born of his mother and instructed by his teachers. What we demand of a machine in order to consider it intelligent is here also similar to what we demand of a student, that is, the ability to function independently of instructors. In the case of the student, this means that he should be able to answer questions without prompting by his teacher. In the case of the machine, this means that once it is originally programmed it should be able to answer questions without having to be reprogrammed by someone knowing the question and answer. It is irrelevant that the method for solving the problem was invented by human beings and built into the operation of the machine. After all, the methods for doing arithmetic were invented long ago and must be taught to each student, but we do not claim that it requires no intelligence to utilize them. The alternative, that a man or machine could somehow be intelligent without benefit of teaching or programming, seems a rather too superficial view to be advanced seriously.

The functional definition of intelligence used above does not necessarily include all aspects of human intelligence. Nevertheless, the ability to answer questions is one important aspect of intelligence, and it is by no means the only part of human intelligence that can be duplicated or surpassed artificially. I have chosen machines that can answer questions because they are the most straightforward example to analyze, and because they raise the ethical problems I wish to illustrate.

If we accept the fact that the human brain, and hence human intelligence are produced by a sequence of physical and chemical processes, it is difficult to see how there can be any general argument against the possibility of producing intelligent machines. One may, of course, argue about the difficulty of doing this, or the timetable for accomplishing it. Living systems have certain functional advantages over man-made systems, including their use of ultramicroscopic or molecular components such as parts of cells to carry out operations like switching, but this advantage is being overcome as electronic technology becomes miniaturized.[13] On the other hand, artificial systems also have their advantages, such as being able to use materials that are rare in nature, which are used in some transistors. It is therefore unlikely that one could show on purely technological grounds that the construction of intelligent machines is impossible.

This is not to imply that we know how to do this at present. Although a number of approaches are being actively considered, it is hard to tell which, if any, of them will lead to intelligent machines. But if we assume that at least one approach will succeed, it is only a small step to the recognition that there is no reason why a machine's intelligence should be limited to that of a man. The suggestion that a machine could be no more intelligent than its creator is as unconvincing as the statement that a student cannot be more intelligent than his parents and teachers. Let us imagine that a machine can be built that will perform certain operations that will enable it to function as if it were highly intelligent according to our definition of answering questions. Clearly, the builder of the machine need not be able to answer the questions in order to design the machine, just as the builder of a crane need not be able to lift the weights that the crane will lift. Thus the advent of intelligent machines is likely to be followed closely by the advent of superintelligent machines, and presumably other machines will be devised that can first equal and then surpass humans at the performance of other activities hitherto reserved to us, such as artistic creation. These possibilities present human society with both new opportunities and new problems.

The technological unemployment that computers may create has been recognized for some time, although there is still discussion over how serious a problem this really is. It is obvious, however, that automation has made many specific jobs obsolete, and the fact that the holders of these jobs have (at least statistically) been able to find new work is more of a tribute to the power of the labor movement than a denial of the impact of automation. It is fairly likely that if only technological considerations had been involved, automation could have progressed more rapidly. Fortunately our economy is to some extent run to benefit human beings, rather than on grounds of abstract efficiency. But the problem of unemployment caused by automation cannot be discussed in this context alone; it is part of the deeper question of possible ways of life in an affluent world.

There is a direct way in which intelligent machines, or simply more efficient computers, could benefit mankind: they could help provide enough material goods to enable the whole world to live at a decent standard. A great deal has been written on this point, and here it will suffice to say that, to the extent to which machines that can duplicate or surpass human beings in specific functions can be made, the restrictions on productivity stemming from human scarcity can be eliminated. The remaining restrictions would then come only from the physical laws governing matter and from the quantities of matter and energy available to us.

These restrictions should not prevent us from ensuring an adequate standard of living for the world's population, provided that the population does not continue to grow exponentially for several generations. If the present population increase continues, it will rapidly outstrip the available supplies of matter and energy, however they may be augmented. Nevertheless, one may hope that before this comes to pass most of the world's people will have accepted birth control as a desirable method for regulating population growth —a development that should be assisted by advances in biological engineering, which will make it possible for the children that are born to approximate the ideal characteristics their parents desire for them.

Some people, however, consider even the promise of effortless affluence that the development of superior computers holds out a not unmixed blessing, particularly those who still believe that human psychology is relatively immutable and that some kind of work for one's livelihood is a necessity for the well-being of both the individual and society.[14] Others feel that work is a means by which men earn the time to do those things that are really desirable, such as play, self-expression through creation, etc. For these people, a development that would release men from the need for working would be wholly beneficial, except for possible side effects such as cluttering up the landscape with machines.

The disagreement apparent here is to a certain extent based on a difference in opinion on the proper goals of humanity. It is unlikely that this can be resolved until the difference is made explicit, which has not so far been the case. On the one hand, the proponents of work as a necessity have implicitly assumed that men require some external constraint on their actions to keep their personalities from degenerating into slothful indifference, a constraint that has been historically provided by the necessity of earning a living. On the other hand, those who would do away with work assume, again implicitly, that the ideal world would be one in which each individual could follow his own dictates on the disposition of his time, without any responsibilities to society.

It would be helpful if the two sides could confront each other on this deeper level and attempt to see where their positions lead. It is by no means clear that working for a living is the only, or even the best, way to ensure the kind of personality that the first group considers desirable. Conversely, there are many commitments that society might properly require of its members distinct from contributing to economic production, such as a contribution to some group effort devoted to an end other than simple survival. The two positions, which appear difficult to reconcile if they are taken as ultimate commitments, may not be so firm if the assumptions underlying them are brought into the open. When this is done, the problem is reduced to a choice of ethical priorities, and it may be that there is much less disagreement between people on this level.

The possible development of intelligent or creative machines, however, raises problems of a different type. One, which is well known, is the possibility that the machines might get out of control and take over the running of the world. This, I think, involves the construction of something other than intelligent machines, which might be called willful machines, and I hope it is clear from my criterion for machine intelligence that a machine does not have to have any kind of independent will in order to be called intelligent. I do not know if machines with an independent will could be built at all, since I do not think we really understand what will is.

The main problem that the existence of intelligent and creative machines would pose to mankind would not be a possible control of man but a loss of what has been a major role of many human beings in the world. Until now, men whose ultimate concern was with ideas or art, could rely on the fact that, whatever the determining features of other parts of human life, in this area the ultimate authority was the human mind and spirit. I think that many men have been attracted to "the life of the mind" by precisely the fact that the individual mind was the source of innovation as well as the judge of merit, which is not to say that no other motives, such as altruism, response to challenge, and curiosity, are involved in devoting oneself to some cultural pursuit. Nevertheless, if machines are developed that provide alternative sources for innovation in the creative activities that have been man's own province, this will have a serious effect on human interest in these areas, particularly when machines can excel the best human performances, as judged by man's own standards.

I would guess that a common reaction to this would be that people taking part in such activities as art, music, and literature would no longer take their own and other human efforts seriously, but rather, like the Sunday artist, paint or write or compose for their own pleasure, rather than with any hope of accomplishing anything in the way of high art. While the various forms of art might continue as human activities under these circumstances, their meaning to the most gifted of their practitioners would have changed significantly. It would be interesting to know how the audience for art would react to work of the highest quality produced by machine. Some people seem to find the personality of the artist a crucial part of their artistic experience with a work, while others do not consider this important.[15] This suggests that an audience for human art might remain even in the situation envisaged, while the artistic output of creative machines would also have its audience.

The same problems would arise in connection with scientific advances made by intelligent machines. For many scientists, research, like artistic creation, is a form of individual expression. To these men, science is not so much an attempt to understand natural phenomena as an effort to create ideas that are in harmony with the way things are—an attitude Einstein expressed when he said,[16] "The axiomatic basis of theoretical physics cannot be extracted from experience, but must be freely invented." Theoretical scientists with this point of view are not simply trying to find patterns in given phenomena, but are in some sense imposing order on the universe, and it seems likely that they would react negatively to intelligent machines that made scientific discoveries.

Even if one's interest in scientific advance is dispassionate, in the sense of wanting to understand natural phenomena without being concerned with the process of discovery, there could be problems with machine-made science. I have indicated that the intelligent machines might not think the way we do, in the sense of either using similar elements, or going through parallel processes to reach a given conclusion. A machine could therefore satisfy my criterion of intelligence if it could answer correctly any given question about the outcome of an observation without being able to explain to us how it came to this conclusion.

From the human standpoint, such a machine would have many of the attributes of the legendary oracles; it would be able to make correct predictions without having any general theory that it could communicate to us. From the standpoint of the machines, humans might appear stupid, in the sense that they would not see the obvious relations between phenomena that the machine utilizes in making its predictions. Such a difference of opinion would be irrelevant if science consisted simply of making correct predictions. Human scientists have, however, always wanted another kind of understanding as well, which involves the general principles relating different aspects of the world. If oracular machines were devised that could make correct predictions without being able to convey any general principles to us, our whole notion of the comprehensibility of the world would probably undergo a radical change, with results that are difficult to foresee.

One consequence could be a loss of interest in science and rational thought in general. If men came to believe that some of the fundamental principles that govern the universe were beyond our comprehension, at least in our present form, they might give up trying to find these principles. Other responses are, however, also possible, especially if man's capacities can be modified by biological engineering. And there is the possibility of some kind of symbiosis between man and machine, which could enhance the capabilities of each for scientific investigation or other activities. Any of these responses might be desirable under certain circumstances, but it is hard to choose among them without some knowledge of the goal we are trying to achieve.

Intelligent or creative machines could be of great value to the human race as well as raising problems for it. Some of the technological advances we may wish to make may be greatly facilitated by the aid of such machines, particularly if the advance requires the solution of problems involving a great many complicated factors. This type of problem has historically been the kind most resistant to human solution, and if we are interested in a definite result, such as a numerical answer, the machines may be much better than we are at solving them.

There is perhaps a still more important role intelligent machines could fill; they could provide an independent form of consciousness with which we could compare ourselves. Because they would have a different way of looking at the world, intelligent machines might lead us to expand our own point of view and perhaps recognize aspects of the world we had previously missed. This is the same thing considered above as a problem raised by the machines, looked at from another standpoint. This ambiguity is in my opinion inherent in the notion of intelligence independent of humanity and also applies to the possible discovery of intelligent extraterrestrial life forms.

The reactions of men to alien intelligences, whether artificial or extraterrestrial, are not likely to be uniform, and it would be well to explore them hypothetically before the situation actually faces us. From the affirmative point of view, the existence of intelligent machines would do something to relieve the spiritual loneliness that comes from being the only sentient beings in the known universe. The extent to which this feeling is present varies from person to person, as does the opposite feeling of importance because of our uniqueness. Nevertheless, I am convinced that it is sufficiently common to be a relevant factor in the determination of whether or not to proceed in the direction of artificial intelligence.

Since intelligent machines could have important effects on the lives of many people, it is within the function of society to control their development, even though this may interfere with the pursuits of some scientists. The pursuit of new knowledge is, after all, subject to constraints because of other human interests, as indicated by the fact that biologists and psychologists are not allowed to experiment freely on human beings. The problem is therefore not whether society is justified in deciding how the development of intelligent machines should proceed, but rather what principles it should follow in making the decisions.

The decisions that must be made about computers will be of two kinds, involving their development and deployment respectively. Only the second has, to my knowledge, been considered in detail by previous authors. To some extent the research effort involved in developing more effective computers has not until now been expensive enough to require massive government support, and there has therefore been little occasion for society to exercise any control over computer development. This will probably change when a serious effort is made to develop computers that compare to man in their intellectual functions. This is likely to be quite expensive, and in view of the extreme effects that superintelligent computers might have on human society, one would expect society, through its government, to play an important role in controlling their development. It would be unfortunate, however, if society in exercising this control allowed the potentialities for harm inherent in such machines to blind it to their potential contribution to human life and rejected their development out of hand.

As with most of the other irreversible decisions to be discussed here, there is an open-ended aspect to the development of intelligent machines; one can control what will happen only up to a point and then other elements over which we have no control enter in. This prospect may seem foreboding enough to warrant suppressing this line of development. Yet this might be the wrong decision. It depends on where we want to go.

The positive factors that could result from artificial intelligence, such as a new form of consciousness, would, if certain human goals were chosen, outweigh the possible loss of control involved in making intelligent computers. Indeed this very abdication of human control over the direction of events might be regarded as a positive step by some, especially those who feel that the proper concern of mankind is the complex psychic world within each person. The desire to be the master of one's fate is not universal among men, even in the West, where a few centuries ago this would have been regarded as dangerous heresy.

In short, the development of artificial intelligence raises a number of hitherto unconsidered moral problems whose resolution is likely to require a careful consideration of the fundamental objectives of human life. Since the decisions involved may become necessary in the not too distant future, one would hope that the discussion about the computer and its effects would reach this new level soon, rather than remaining on the mainly pragmatic level that has characterized it so far. It is possible that the clarification of human goals would have a helpful effect on computer research as well. Even within the general area of intelligent machines, there may be many different directions that can be pursued. As some of these will be more relevant to some human goals than others, a decision about goals would provide guidance for choosing among the directions. To the objection that this would be an unwarranted interference with free research, one can answer only that such an interference has been implicit in almost all external support of applied research in modern times. In any case, it is to be hoped that the research scientists involved in extending the capabilities of computers will play a role in the formulation of the goals that will guide the research they will do.

AN END TO AGING AND DEATH

Another possibly impending technological development is a major increase in the active human life span, by which I mean that human beings would remain in good physical condition for periods of several hundreds or thousands of years. Although this development might strictly speaking be a part of what I have called biological engineering, I think it is sufficiently interesting and its implications sufficiently far-reaching to discuss in itself.

The elimination of aging and death has been a human dream since the earliest written records, such as the *Epic of Gilgamesh*. In spite of this, no substantial practical advances toward this goal have yet been made. Although in the advanced countries the death rates in all age groups have decreased significantly in this century,[17] even today few men can look forward to more than, say, ninety years of active life. Because of the apparent inevitability of age and death, many have concluded that nothing can be done about this situation and have convinced themselves that death is a desirable aspect of life.

There is also the religious response to death, which in many cases takes the form of assuming some kind of survival of physical death or an afterlife. Since no scientific evidence for this hypothesis has been evinced until now, I will disregard this possibility here.

The causal connection between aging and death is not clear, since death also occurs in the young and is usually the result of some specific cause rather than a generalized condition of old age. Nevertheless, with increased age there is a decrease in the functioning of various parts of the body and a deterioration of the repair-mechanism, which makes one more vulnerable to death by one or another of the causes that can

afflict both young and old.[18] Bacterial pneu-
monia, for example, which has a "known" cure,
nevertheless kills a fraction of the elderly population each year, probably because of their lower
general resistance. It therefore seems reasonable
to expect that if the process of aging could be
halted or slowed, it would lead to a great decrease in the death rate of the chronologically
old, and hence a major increase in the average
life span.

As mentioned earlier, the cause of aging, or
even what the process involves on a cellular or a
molecular level, is not conclusively known. The
question of whether individual cells can survive
and divide indefinitely, which was once thought
to have been answered affirmatively by the experiments of Alexis Carrel, is now again considered
an open one.[19] Some biologists now believe they
have evidence that individual cells have a finite
life span even if supplied with food and oxygen
and can undergo only a fixed number of divisions
before dying.

Opinion among those working in the field appears divided between the view that aging is a
reaction of the organism to external stimuli,
which accumulate during the life span and eventually cause irreparable damage, and the view
that it is the result of a built-in mechanism genetically controlled like the other life processes.[20]
The fact that the rate of aging is roughly constant within a given species while it varies by
many orders of magnitude between species is one
bit of evidence in favor of the genetic hypothesis.

If aging is genetically controlled and therefore induced by specific chemical reactions in the cells, the prospect of eliminating it by outside interference with these chemical reactions seems fairly bright, particularly if the mechanism of aging is a chemical repressor acting on some section of the cell DNA responsible for the repair function. If this is so, it would be necessary to "repress the repressors" in order to avoid aging, and techniques for doing this, once the relevant reactions were identified, would probably not be far behind.

In a more advanced stage of biological understanding, it might also be possible to reverse some of the effects of aging that had already taken place, since these too involve definite physical and chemical changes. It is sometimes stated that certain biological changes that occur during aging are irreversible, implying that nothing can be done about them. This use of the term irreversible is apparently different from its use in thermodynamics, where it implies only that energy must be supplied from the outside to a system in order to recover the initial state. In the presence of such an outside source of energy, there are no literally irreversible reactions in physics, and it is difficult to see why there should be in biology either.

It therefore seems at least a serious possibility that the development of biology will enable us to eliminate aging and make it possible for human beings to maintain themselves indefinitely at whatever biological age they choose. This in turn would presumably lead to an increase in the life span far beyond anything seen until now, perhaps by several orders of magnitude. The latter effect would be enhanced by a simultaneous advance in dealing with those individual diseases that afflict the young as well as the old. If these could be eliminated as well, the sources of death would be essentially reduced to accidents and individual choice.

If the prospect of bodily immortality is a serious one, then it becomes necessary to examine the consequences of this development for the life of individuals and for society. One might naïvely imagine that the prospect of indefinite life at the age of one's choice would be greeted with almost universal acclaim. The reactions of people to the suggestion that this possibility exists have, however, often been extremely negative, both for themselves as individuals and for the world.[21] It is therefore important to consider some of the possible positive and negative aspects of a great increase in the useful life span.

Some of the advantages are obvious. Under present circumstances, almost all measurable physical and biological functions reach their peak at an early age, usually between fifteen and twenty-five, and then decline slowly.[22] Those who chose to remain at a physiological age in this range would therefore stay at the height of their functional abilities indefinitely and would not be in the position of having to substitute experience and wisdom for ability as they grew older. At present the accumulated experience of a long lifetime is usually wasted because of the death of the individual who bears it. If the active life span were increased manyfold, it is likely that simply working longer with the benefit of this experience would lead to new heights of creative achievement. Imagine what Beethoven or Newton might have accomplished had they been able to retain their full abilities for hundreds or thousands of years.

Another value of long life would be the opening of new possibilities requiring a long time span. There are many people who would wish to do things for which they have little talent, such as musical performance. Given enough time, it might be possible for such people to attain a satisfactory level of achievement even in the absence of talent. Given a hundred years to spend, almost anyone might learn to play the organ to his satisfaction. With enough time, even some activities that one wouldn't ordinarily imagine become possible. By spending forty years at it, Simon Rodia was able singlehandedly to create the Watts Towers, a work that would otherwise have taken many men to achieve.[23] If forty years were only a small fraction of one's life, such enterprises could become feasible even to those lacking Rodia's single-minded dedication. This development might have profound effects on the relationship between individuals, and between individuals and society, in that it would change the balance between what can be done by the individual and what can be done only by groups.

A third positive effect of much longer life

might be the alleviation of the fear of death, which is at the root of so many human institutions. I say "might be" because it is conceivable that if people lived much longer they would become more rather than less afraid of death. But under the assumption I have made that the only causes of death would be accident or choice, it seems reasonable to conclude that people's attitude toward death would become quite different than it is now, when death is a certainty in a fairly definite time period. While a preoccupation with death may not be apparent in everyday affairs, it has been observed that a concern with death permeates our society and shows up in many indirect ways in our culture.[24] I would guess that the elimination of this constant fear on everyone's mental horizon would act as a tremendous liberating force on the human mind and would result in people much better balanced psychologically than we are at present.

A final advantage of the elimination of aging is that it would remove what appears to me the most important example of an aspect of life beyond human control. An increasing control over nature has characterized human history, but man's own life cycle has until now been an exception. If this too could be brought under man's control, it would be a crucial step in the establishment of man's mastery over the world. This is not to say that man would have no limitations if death is conquered, since both his powers and his imagination are finite. These, however, are internal limitations rather than arbitrary impositions from outside. Until now, the philosophical reaction to the tyranny of death was at best a proud disregard, first stated by Epicurus and expressed in perhaps its loftiest form by Bertrand Russell in his essay, "A Free Man's Worship."[25] If death is no longer inevitable, another, more affirmative philosophy is possible and will surely be forthcoming. This in turn will influence man's life and goals in ways that are not obvious.

But people have also cited disadvantages of the elimination of aging and death. It would severely disrupt a society whose institutions are built around the fact that its members usually live about seventy years. Such institutions as the family and government would have to be radically modified in a world without aging; the system of retirement at a fixed chronological age would have to be completely changed. Many people, when faced with the necessity for such changes in the oldest and most firmly rooted institutions in our society, despair of creating a viable world without them and reject out of hand the development that would necessitate the changes.

The force of this objection is questionable if one recognizes that the institutions in question seem so natural precisely because they fit the needs of the present state of man, and we have been brought up within their framework. If the state of man can change, then other institutions, which better suit the new state, would come to seem equally natural, especially to new generations. The transition from old to new might be difficult, but there is no reason to despair of the

possibility of devising the new institutions necessary.

Another objection to the desirability of indefinite life arises from the assumption that mental growth would not continue even if physiological aging were eliminated. One argument cited in
favor of this is the fact that the brain cells do not
regenerate in adults, so that the total number de-
creases with chronological aging, or at least does
not increase. Another is that mental habits, or
patterns of thought, get set when one is fairly
young and can be changed only with difficulty,
if at all, in later life. If the primary assumption
is granted, it follows that if aging were eliminated,
the world would become filled with physically
young, mentally rigid people who would be unable either to do anything new or creative or to
accept such innovations proposed by others. This
would be particularly bad if such people were
able to remain in positions of authority through
their greater chronological age or through the
power and wealth they had accumulated.

It is difficult to know how valid the premises
on which this objection is based are. While a
decrease in mental flexibility is common in old
people, this may be related to the physical
changes taking place in their bodies, such as a
diminished blood supply to the brain because of
hardening of the arteries. If this physical deterioration were eliminated, it could be that mental
growth would continue as it does in the young. If
this should turn out not to be the case, and the
setting of mental patterns in the experienced

should prove to be an inherent psychological effect, at least in humans as they are now constructed, there is still the possibility that a different type of training, in which openness of mind was stressed, or else some application of biological engineering to the human brain, could produce people who did not attain unalterable views through experience. If no such methods work and the chronologically aged necessarily stop growing mentally, many people would still feel that life offers enough other pleasures to make it worth living. In that case, the society would have to be arranged so that intellectual activity was the work of the relatively young, and the elderly were left to enjoy physical pleasures.

There is also the problem of overpopulation. Even with the present average life span the world's population is doubling every forty years, and some form of birth control seems necessary. If everyone lived much longer than they do now, the population would grow much faster than it does now, unless more stringent restrictions on reproduction were enforced. Many people oppose this on the ground that it sacrifices the right of future generations to be born to the privilege of those now alive to remain alive. It is also argued that the desire to have children is a fundamental human motivation and severe psychological disturbances would result, particularly among women, if this desire were frustrated.

To some extent this problem is already upon us. A doubling of the population every forty years cannot long continue, no matter what technological advances occur, since at this rate, in a mere six thousand years, all of the matter in the visible universe would become incorporated into human bodies.[26] The problem of overpopulation is, however, caused not by the survival to a great age of parents, but rather by the number of children they produce that survive to childbearing age. Let us suppose everybody lived to the age of one thousand years and then died. Suppose further that during this period each woman bore exactly two children, say when she was twenty and twenty-five years old. It is easy to see that, rather than doubling every forty years, the population would instead at first increase linearly with time, eventually reach a maximum of about fifty times the original population in one thousand years, and then remain roughly constant. The condition for eventual stability of population is that the average woman during her life produce two children that survive to adulthood and no more. At present, the number produced is closer to three, causing the geometric increase in population. No matter how long each person lives, so long as they die sometime, the reproduction rate per lifetime need not drop below two per woman in order to keep the population from growing exponentially. And if the population does eventually stabilize, one can expect technology to be able to support it at a reasonable standard of living.

To avoid overpopulation it is therefore necessary to limit the average number of children per lifetime to about two per woman. This is the case either in our present world, or in a world where people live ten thousand years. The major difference between the two situations for the individual would be that at present the period of childbearing and childraising forms a major portion of the total life span, whereas if the life span becomes very long and the number of children remains small, only a small part of one's life would be devoted to raising children. Whether this would lead to severe psychological problems is not clear. But there is no question of having to eliminate reproduction for most people in order to pay for long life. This kind of change in the pattern of reproduction, combined with a great increase in the life span, would have several effects on society. There would be relatively few chronologically young people in the population. This might not make a great difference if the rigidity of thought patterns discussed above could be avoided. If it could not, and innovation still depended on the chronologically young, then the rate of innovation in human life would presumably slow down. This is one of the choices that the possibility of long life could bring before us.

Although both sides can produce plausible arguments as to the desirability of an increased span of youthful life, what is really at issue here is the purposes of human life. A world in which people did not age and lived indefinitely would be a very different one in almost every respect from the present one. It is an intellectual error to consider such a world in the context of small changes from the present one. Instead, it would be better to work out the way things might be under such conditions without assuming that any particular institution of our world would necessarily survive. The hypothetical society as constructed might appeal more to those who consider the present human condition tragic than to those who are relatively satisfied with it. The point is that in addition to citing specific objections and advantages it would be wise to analyze the consequences of life extension in terms of ultimate human goals and their possible conflicts. Only then could we have a realistic idea of the sacrifices that might be necessary to allow people to live much longer, and know whether they would be something we could tolerate.

The decision about whether or not the elimination of aging would be desirable is by no means a hypothetical moral problem, in the sense that no consequences follow from it. Once it is within technical possibility to do something about the rate of aging, there is likely to be intense public pressure to sponsor a crash program of research to fulfill this possibility, and the prospective supporters of such research, i.e., the government and perhaps some large foundations, will have to decide what to do. There may also be an intermediary period during which aging control will have to be carefully monitored, to look for possible side effects, which might involve a good deal of interference with the lives of individual citizens. And since a viable society in which aging does not occur will involve many changes from the present society, the process of getting from here to there is likely to be a painful one, in which the individual steps may appear regressive or arbitrary to many people, unless the goal to be attained remains in sight.

One characteristic of any "world-shaking decision" is that its implementation will involve far-reaching transformations of society, in which many familiar institutions will change or disappear. When such radical changes are considered, it is important to ask what will remain fixed, or, put a little differently, what purposes are being served by the transformation. A good practical definition of ultimate human goals is those aims that we want to remain fixed under the transformations of society that are being considered. If there are no fixed points of this kind, then we have no logical way to exclude any transformation of society, and we will probably be unhappily surprised at what we get.

We could regard the elimination of aging and death either as an end in itself or as a means to attaining other ends that are difficult or impossible within our current life pattern. In the former case, we must ask what other ends this one might conflict with and try to come to some accommodation between them. In the latter, the ends should be discussed to see whether they are really served by the development we are considering and also whether they are in conflict with other ends. In either case, an explanation of ultimate human goals is essential in order to make a rational decision.

Let us consider some specific choices of human

goals that could help us decide whether the elimination of aging is a good thing to work toward. Some people believe that the greatest good would be for each individual to enjoy in the fullest possible way the pleasures of both body and mind that are the province of healthy and wealthy young people: food, drink, sex, love, idle (as opposed to systematic) thought, games, etc. If one accepts this particular vision of the world and the attainment of it as the ultimate goal, then the elimination of aging and death, which at present render all such delights temporary, would indeed be a desirable development. In fact, one of the arguments that has been often used to counter hedonism as a philosophy of life is that it does not prepare one for the inevitable aging and death that one must face. Hence a hedonist might well see in this scientific advance a welcome answer to the objection to his views.

Other goals would not always lead to this conclusion. The Buddhist doctrine that human life is one of suffering and that escape from this form of existence is the ultimate good to be striven for, would hardly see an extension of man's life on earth as desirable, at least on the face of things, although Buddhists might consider an extended life valuable because of the expanded possibilities for spiritual development. It is also possible that some of the necessary by-products of an extended life span, such as birth control, might conflict with other long-range goals; it has been suggested that those to be born in the future will be capable of higher forms of happiness than those

alive now, so that preventing their birth in order
that we may survive would be in conflict with a
general goal of maximizing the total happiness
over long periods of time.[27] While certain implicit assumptions in this argument may be questioned, it probably contains a kernel of the objection many people feel toward controlling births
in order to benefit the present generation in any
respect.

People's reactions to the desirability of extended life are so strong and so varied that the
question cannot and should not be treated on an
ad hoc basis of short-term considerations. This
question is so tied up with the foundations of our
life that almost any ultimate human goal might
have some bearing on it. If our goals remain tacit
or unformulated, then when aging control becomes possible, severe disturbances may result
within society from disagreements about whether
or not it should be put into effect. It seems highly
unlikely that a viable society could exist in which
part of the population remained young while
another part grew old. In order to avoid such
stresses within the society, there must be some
general agreement in advance on what is to be
done. And this will be possible only if there is a
prior agreement on general human goals.

SOME OTHER TECHNICAL POSSIBILITIES

Many other technological developments that may
occur in the next one or two centuries could re-

sult in thoroughgoing transformations of human life. One would be the detection of radio signals from intelligent beings in another stellar system,[28] which would not necessarily mean that the alien beings knew of our existence, since they might send out signals like an earthly radio station, for whoever is there to listen. Therefore, we have the option of whether to attempt communication by returning signals to them. Such communication might not be possible even if both sides make the effort to do so. We have no experience in communicating with beings that have different senses, and a completely different set of concepts for analyzing the world than we do. Yet this may very well be the case with any alien intelligent species that we contact. The attempt to communicate might be worthwhile just to find out if it is possible at all.

In addition to such unknown matters of fact, there is a disagreement involving basic goals here as well. Cogent arguments have been presented both for and against attempting communication. One group of writers emphasizes the dangers involved if the aliens prove inimical to man and technologically superior to him. They also stress the advantage in having one culture proceed independently of other superior cultures, even if the latter are not actively antagonistic, citing the bad effects of contacts between white men and Polynesians as a parallel to what might happen to mankind if it met a superior alien race.[29]

Another group gives illustrations from earthly experience of the benefits of contact with a tech-

nically superior group, sometimes using the same
examples used negatively by the other side. They
cite the new knowledge that can be gained by
such contact, the possible unifying effect on humanity of being faced with an alien intelligence,
and the testing of existing social and political patterns of behavior by a recognition of how paro-
chial they are.[30]

Some of these considerations are similar to
those involved in the creation of artificial intelligence, which is also nonhuman. A superior alien
species that would answer all our questions about
the world might make life a good deal easier for
us, but this would preclude the pleasure some of
us obtain from creative thought. If, however, we
are fundamentally dissatisfied with human life in
its present form, we might be willing to accept
such changes, in the hope that they would lead
to something better. In view of such alternatives,
it would be helpful to think about our goals before deciding to answer or not answer any communications from other stellar systems.

Another possible development which raises
questions concerning ultimate goals is the use of
chemical or electrical stimulation of the human
brain to produce new patterns of mental activity.
Chemicals that affect the consciousness have been
known for some time, but they have received new
attention lately because of the increasing use of
psychedelic drugs such as LSD. Since all the
known psychedelic drugs were discovered acci-
dentally, and drugs with still more profound ef-

fects can probably be devised once the physiological mechanisms of drug action on the brain are understood, it is obvious that the problems involved here are just beginning.

Regrettably most opponents of the use of psychedelic drugs have argued as if the ethics needed to evaluate the use of these drugs was quite clear and the only questions were the objective effects of the drugs.[31] Proponents of the drugs could well argue that even if they have the bad effects cited by their critics, such as a loss of interest in the usual human activities or chromosome damage, the form of the psychic life they stimulate is worth the risk. It is hard to disprove this argument without some decision about what kinds of life society should encourage its members to live. But such a discussion has not been prominent in the writings on this issue.

It must be admitted that the best known proponents of the use of LSD have made little effort to communicate their arguments in meaningful terms and therefore have not been taken very seriously by those for whom verbal communication is important. One may hope that this situation will change and a detailed ethical alternative to ordinary life involving the systematic use of drugs will be formulated. When this is done it will be possible to consider the alternatives on the basis of what forms of individual activity are to be ruled out by society as inadmissible. But in order to decide this rationally, we must have some vision of what a human being should be, which again is related to our ultimate goals as a species.

Very similar questions would be raised by the invention of electrical methods for pleasurable stimulation of the brain, or what have sometimes been called "dream machines." These are devices that, by direct electrical action on areas of the brain, would produce sensations comparable to, or even stronger than, those produced indirectly in ordinary life by such activities as eating, sex, hearing music, etc. It may indeed be possible artificially to induce mental states corresponding to any imaginable human experience without the need for undergoing the experience itself; experiments with animals and humans offer some evidence that the induction of mental states through such electrical stimulation is feasible.

The danger of such a development is, of course, that many people might wish to devote their time to the pleasures that would be made available through these machines, disregarding "real life" altogether. It would obviously be difficult for society to function if a large fraction of its members were so involved, although it might not be impossible if enough work could be automated. The question of whether such a development is desirable, however, depends on its possible conflict with other images of what human life should be. If there is a serious possibility that dream machines would be attractive enough to lure most of humanity from other pursuits, then we must determine where we want to go before we decide whether or not to allow their development and use.

I firmly believe that in trying to predict the future of technology reality is likely to outstrip one's most extreme vision. The situations postulated here raise fundamental ethical questions. This is likely to be even more true for the technological advances we do not foresee. In these situations, which will come upon us with much less warning, it will be still more essential that we be confident about our long-term goals in order to know how to implement the technological possibilities.

IV. A Classification and Analysis of Goals

Perhaps the most fundamental division between long-range goals is between goals that involve the intensification or fulfillment of something already to some extent present in humanity and goals that require the creation or achievement of something qualitatively new. Goals of the first type are easier to formulate precisely, since there are models available for the result we are seeking. Goals of the second type are like visions of a place we have never seen, and their expression depends strongly on our imagination. We might call the first type developmental goals, and the second transcendent goals. In this sense the goals envisaged by most nonreligious writers are developmental, while those of the leading religions are often transcendent.

To say that a goal is developmental does not mean that it will not involve qualitative changes in human life. Suppose we wished to give all men the intelligence of Newton and the sensitivity of Goethe.[1] Since these models already exist, the goal would be developmental, even though a very different way of life might ensue for the rest of mankind if it were achieved. Developmental goals can involve either the perfection of some human trait or activity considered desirable, or the elimination of one considered undesirable. The first category would include such goals as the extension to all of humanity of the high intelligence displayed by such men as Newton or an even higher intelligence never yet achieved. The second category could be illustrated by the goal of eliminating all suffering in human life. Since parts at least of many men's lives do not involve such suffering, it is possible to use these as models to formulate what the absence of suffering would mean for everyone.

Those who consider only developmental long-range goals tacitly assume that the human situation as it presently exists, at least for some people, is a fair approximation of the best that can be achieved, or at least can now be conceived. They therefore concentrate on the extrapolation of aspects already present in human life or the wider extension of these aspects within the population. In contrast, the proposers of transcendent goals assume that something much better than the present life of man can be achieved by a radical innovation of something that does not at present exist in human life. They reject the plaint of Ecclesiastes that "there is nothing new under the sun" as an unjustified conclusion and follow instead the poet who wrote:[2]

> *Ah Love, could you and I with fate conspire*
> *To grasp this sorry scheme of things entire*
> *Would we not shatter it to bits and then*
> *Remold it nearer to the Heart's desire!*

In a sense, developmental and transcendent goals might be regarded as successive stages in a process of going from where man is now to what he will become. But this may not be the order in which things will or should be done.

The formulation of transcendent goals is difficult because the lack of models makes it hard to imagine what conditions would really be like in the new situation. Consider, for example, the proposal that men would be much better off if they all shared a common consciousness, perhaps through something like an artificial telepathic communication system. While it is possible to describe this in words, and perhaps even to carry out the plan, it is very difficult to feel intuitively what life would be like for those who lived under these conditions. The proposers of the plan do not have a shared consciousness and therefore are not recommending something they know to be good by direct experience or by the testimony of other people they trust. Instead, they are relying on analogy or other rational processes to conclude that if there were such a mental linkup between people, it would seem worth while to those sharing it.

I think it is as much for this reason as because of the difficulty of attainment that many people, particularly in the modern world, have been suspicious of transcendent goals. They distrust them because there is no guarantee that the condition once realized would really be desirable. I doubt that any general conclusion can be reached concerning the validity of such doubts, beyond considering each proposal on its merits and seeing what flaws may be inherent in it. Money-back guarantees are not usually available for human plans.

Do We Change the Environment, Man, or Our Minds?

The next important division among goals has to do with the modification of individual men. The proposers of some goals take man's present characteristics as fixed points and concern themselves with changes in the world outside of man, which indeed may react back on man, but usually in relatively peripheral ways. Other goals are based on the assumption that man as he presently exists must be modified in specified ways in order to reach the desired end. A third category of goals rejects the modification of both man and his environment—the former as unnecessary, the latter as irrelevant—and emphasizes instead the importance of already present aspects of man that are insufficiently cultivated in most people.

It may seem paradoxical that the human race would wish to consider goals for itself that would result in its own alteration, perhaps into something qualitatively different, but I do not believe that any real contradiction is involved. In any transformation, some features remain unchanged, and presumably if a goal that involves the transformation of man is consciously chosen, we will choose to preserve those things about ourselves we consider essential and desirable. Somewhat analogous situations already occur in the life of an individual, such as the choice to undergo psychotherapy or plastic surgery. Therefore, if we decide that something is lacking in all men, there is no reason why we should not set about introducing it, even if this makes us into something new.

We might call goals that involve a change in the outside world environmental goals; goals that require a modification of man, reconstructive goals; and goals that involve a change of emphasis as much as of substance, divertive goals.

As a rough generalization, religious thinkers tend to suggest divertive goals, like the Buddha's emphasis on withdrawal from contacts with the outside world to search for inner enlightenment. Secular thinkers on the other hand have often stressed environmental goals, like the socialists' call for a more equitable distribution of wealth. These latter goals are not necessarily meant as long-range goals, however. In some cases they are predicated on the idea that when the environment is changed in the required way, this will in turn produce some desirable change in the nature of man. It is, however, usually unclear what the desired change in man is, or precisely how the new environment will bring it about. For that reason, I will try here to consider environmental goals in their own right, without considering how they may indirectly change man. If such a change is the real aim, then we are dealing with a reconstructive goal, and the question is one of means.

These remarks are not meant as a condemnation of those who have proposed changes in the environment as a way of changing man. Until recently, no better methods appeared to be available, and those who believed that man was imperfect in some respects had to face the very complex problem of the relationship between a change in the environment and the change it produces in man. Many of the debates on the value of some proposed new social or political systems have centered on this question. But with our present imperfect understanding of psychology and the social sciences we cannot yet predict accurately the effects of such indirect methods for changing people.

Until now, the main choices were between modifying the environment to suit better the way man is, and trying to cultivate those human features that are well adjusted to the environment, or relatively independent of it. It is perhaps by allowing a third distinction that the coming developments in biology and psychology will play their greatest role: we may now consider the direct modification of man in specified ways if we deem it desirable.

It is, of course, not easy to know what the feelings of the new form of man would be. We may believe that a man would be happier if his "unconscious" were more directly accessible to his conscious mind and go about constructing a new form of man in which this would be the case. Only he, however, would know how it feels to be "conscious of the unconscious." Here again there are parallel situations in present-day life, such as the decision of an uneducated parent to make sacrifices so that his child can go to college. Those who believe that something essential is lacking in man as he exists will in the same spirit welcome the possibility that it can be instilled into him.

Others, however, may feel differently. They may argue, to follow the analogy, that the child who goes to college may actually be unhappier for having done so, and that in the same way the new man may wish that he were like the old man. This may be a valid argument for proceeding cautiously in the modification of man, but it cannot be taken as a conclusive argument against it.

To illustrate these points let us consider an example of a reconstructive goal. One unfortunate aspect of human life is the incidence of aggression between people, both on an individual scale, as in crimes of violence, and on a national scale, as in wars. There is no general agreement on the causes of aggression; some observers consider it biologically innate,[3] others regard it as the product of conditioning, present in some cultures and absent in others.[4] Suppose it were agreed that humanity would be better off if aggression against other men were impossible. One can imagine psychological or physiological methods by which such a situation could be brought about, or at least approached, and indeed many writers have considered such possibilities as conditioned inhibitions that would operate whenever aggression was attempted. In other words, to bring about a society in which aggression between people does not occur, it might be necessary to introduce specific changes in human mental patterns.

This possibility involves something quite different from the classical exhortation to love one's neighbor, although it has a similar end in mind. The latter is an appeal to a presumed free choice on the part of the individual to choose his behavior pattern to conform to the desired standard. In the new approach man would be redesigned to behave automatically in the way that is chosen. The two approaches reflect two different attitudes toward human freedom. Nevertheless, I do not think that the "engineering" approach can automatically be rejected as immoral. To some extent, much of the education and training of children is an attempt to ensure that particular forms of behavior will not be exhibited. Take, for example, toilet training or the prohibition of incest. It would not seem that any fundamental principle of morality would be violated if the instillation of such prohibitions could be done more efficiently than it is by the present methods. And if mankind should choose to regard aggression with the same loathing as most societies now regard incest, I see no reason why morality would exclude the use of the methods described above to eliminate it. As always, there is the question of the possible effects the modifications in man required to control aggression would have on other aspects of behavior. This is, however, more of a technical than a moral question, and it is hard to see any a priori reason why the effects must be detrimental.

The divertive goals are in some ways the most subtle, since the people who suggest them imply that the activities of most people are inappropriate to what should really concern mankind. The "true" concerns are supposed to reside in other activities, carried out by only a few. An important aspect of divertive goals is that the right activities are to be substituted for the wrong ones through a revision of choice, rather than through a change of ability. Otherwise, the goal would be classified as reconstructive. A typical example of a divertive goal is the mystic's call for concentration upon the world within one's mind. Only a small part of humanity has ever systematically attempted to explore this inner world. Nevertheless, those groups, religious or other, that sponsor mysticism hold that the inner world is accessible to all who choose to explore it, and not just to a selected few.

To reach divertive goals requires a great deal of mental and physical effort on the part of the individual, and they have not usually been thought of as group goals, although sometimes small groups of men have been formed, as in Buddhist monasteries, in the belief that they could by their combined efforts further the individual goal being pursued. In the same way, if humanity adopted individual mystic insight as one of its goals, some reorganizations of society could probably be made to further the goal, and in this sense divertive goals may be thought of as group goals.

Individual Goals and Collective Goals

This suggests a third division among types of goals, those that refer to aspects of the life of individuals, and those that pertain to some activity of a larger group in which the individual is a component. Society's role in reaching individual goals may consist of either helping to bring about the desired situation in which the individual can act, or providing the background in which the desired individual activities take place. In either case it is somewhat passive. In what I will call collective goals, society, or some subgroup of it, becomes the leading actor, and the roles of individuals are secondary, except insofar as they contribute to the activity of the group.

As an analogy for the situation envisaged under individual goals we might take a cooperative store. The members, whose aim is to obtain goods at a low price, represent the individuals in a society, while the cooperative represents the society, which performs various services for the members in pursuit of this goal. A good analogy for collective goals is an amateur football team whose goal is to win the game, an activity of the team as a whole, to which the activities of the individual players must contribute.

A further distinction must be made between individual goals and what could be called personal goals. The latter are goals chosen by individuals for their own lives, without regard to the aims of the society, and could be whatever any person considered worth devoting his life to, from sensual pleasure to the pursuit of knowledge.

This book is not devoted to the search for personal goals, but rather to those goals agreed upon by the human race, be they individual or collective. It is important to recognize that there is no contradiction in the simultaneous existence of personal goals and goals for the human race. The latter should not and will not prescribe all activities of all individuals, any more than the goal of winning a football game prescribes every step each player should take.

Some philosophers have felt that the greatest good was for each man to be able to pursue his personal goals with a minimum of outside interference. A possible goal for the human race would therefore be to bring about a world in which this was the case. This would be an individual goal, since it refers to an activity by the individual members of society, and might be called the goal of total individualism. It represents one extreme of the spectrum of goals; the values it exalts are those of the individuals alive at a given time, whatever their source and wherever they lead. The major constraint on individual actions under the system envisaged in this goal would be that actions of different individuals should not conflict with one another. In this respect, it resembles an abstract mathematical system of axioms whose only constraint is the consistency of the axioms. The goal of total individualism will be analyzed later in some detail, since it makes certain implicit assumptions about human motivations that are subject to scientific investigation.

The divertive goal of achieving individual mystic insight is obviously also an individual goal, but one in which the desirable activities of the individual are prescribed rather than left free. It, too, makes certain assumptions about the nature of man and will be analyzed when we consider some goals that have been proposed in the past.

Collective goals have been less frequently proposed in the past but may be more seriously considered in the future. For example, we might want to devote a major fraction of human effort to the systematic understanding of natural phenomena. This could require major modifications in human intelligence, so that more than a small fraction of the population would be capable of the necessary intellectual effort. This then would be a long-range goal that was both reconstructive and collective, but still developmental.

A novel type of collective goal is the transcendent goal of producing some closer linkup between different human minds than exists at present. This could be thought of as a part of a still longer term goal, going beyond the human race. That is, the extension of consciousness to its logical limit, when it becomes coextensive with the universe. This will be discussed further in the chapter dealing with consciousness.

The Faustian Search as a Goal

One other property of different goals that is useful for classifying them is whether or not a specific end situation is envisaged in the statement of the goal. Most of the goals I have used as examples have fairly definite situations or states as their outcome, but there is also another type. Consider the bargain between Faust and Mephistopheles described by Goethe.[5] Faust offers his soul if Mephistopheles can lead him to a "golden moment" that Faust will find so blissful he will want it to persist forever. What is described here is not a definite state but a search for something Faust is missing but thinks may exist, and possible long-range goals for the human race include this kind of Faustian search for a yet undiscovered state of bliss.

Although with these goals we cannot be sure that what we are seeking can be found, this has not deterred men in the past; scientists search for a comprehensive explanation of natural phenomena with no assurance of success. The main condition for such a search is that the searchers should be convinced that what they are seeking exists, and define some fairly definite procedure of looking for it. They must specify how we are to search, but not necessarily what we are searching for.

Faustian goals with unspecified aims have in the past usually been personal goals, but this is not a necessary limitation. The human race can search for something we will all find good just as an individual can seek something he will find personally good. In the process of searching, humanity will of necessity explore various new forms of experience—in art, science, sensuality, adventure, etc. Temporary goals may emerge along the way, even though the ultimate end is not seen. As long as we remain committed to the search, it will act as a guide to our other actions, just as a well-defined goal would do. In a certain sense, the search itself is the group goal, just as it was for Faust.

Intermediate Goals and Final Goals

There are goals that are clearly way stations en route to something else, and goals that can perhaps be achieved only in the indefinite future, and that may involve more than the human race in their accomplishment. Men vary a good deal in their powers of imagination, and it is to be expected that in their search for goals, some will explore much wider horizons than others.

Ideally, I think we would like to be able to set final goals for ourselves that would provide a direction for human history into the indefinite future, that is, provide an answer to the question: Where is the human race going? They would also make it easier to set up intermediate goals, some of which could be preliminary steps to the final goal. But the limited efforts that I have made with a few others have convinced me that these final goals are much harder to imagine than the intermediate goals, because they refer to the far distant future, which necessarily makes them much more abstract and removed from the situations familiar to us. Nevertheless, because of the great value of final goals if we could formulate and agree on them, I believe it is necessary to consider them along with the search for intermediate goals.

The common feature in all our searches is that the goals should be suitable for all humanity and go beyond our immediate preoccupations. And it is unlikely that there will be a consensus on such goals until a much larger group of people becomes involved in the discussion.

AN ANALYSIS OF GOALS
THAT HAVE BEEN SUGGESTED

Of the number of long-range goals that have been proposed for humanity in the past I will consider chiefly those that come from the teachings of the universal religions and from the writings of philosophers, some of whom were religious believers, others naturalists. I will also consider one goal implicit in much political philosophy, which I call total individualism. Not all the ideas I considered here were directly proposed as goals of the human race. In some cases, like the belief in progress through evolution, it was assumed that the activities would occur naturally, whether or not we chose them. In other cases, the activities proposed referred to individual goals, like the Buddhist aim to eliminate suffering. I have chosen, however, to treat these ideas as if they were current proposals for long-range goals, since I believe that many people would defend them as such.

I have said that I believe that the goals proposed in the past are inadequate because of the misapprehensions about man and the universe of those proposing them. This, of course, does not mean that there is nothing of value for us in these goals; indeed, it is quite possible that some elements of them will enter into whatever goals we choose, and certainly their propounders were among the wisest and best men who have ever lived. But an uncritical acceptance of past goals is unwarranted, as is the assumption that they are the solution to the question raised in this book.

Since it would be impossible to cover all the goals that have been suggested, I have chosen a few characteristic and well-known ones to discuss in detail. The assumptions about man and the world that lie behind them and the flaws that are to be found in them are also relevant to other goals. So perhaps are some of their virtues.

It is useful to consider goals according to the assumptions that go into them. For example, one group assumes some form of survival after death, either through successive reincarnations or through the persistence of an immaterial soul. While different goals can and have been proposed on the basis of this, they are all more similar than goals based on other assumptions.

The assumptions behind past goals have included both statements relating to objective reality, such as the one about survival after death, and statements of how human beings feel, such as Buddha's statement that ordinary human life is suffering. As I understand these statements, they are both in principle verifiable, that is, it would be possible to obtain evidence for or against them by observation, questioning of people, etc. It therefore seems reasonable to treat them as propositions of natural science or social science and compare them to what we have learned about the world. This is the test I will apply, the main basis of comparison being with the scientific principles outlined in Chapter II.

In addition to their assumptions about the world and other objective factors, the proposers of goals make certain ethical assumptions. These I will not comment on in detail. As I have already indicated, one of *my* assumptions is that there is no external standard for ethical statements analogous to the standard of our perceptions for statements about the world. Hence an evaluation of the ethical content of the goals I consider here would be essentially a statement about my own emotions. I do not expect the reader to weigh my emotions more highly than his own, and therefore I leave the evaluation of the ethical content to each reader. An exploration of the areas of ethical agreement among men would be very interesting, but it is beyond the purpose of this book.

To many people, the source of a goal, or of any ethical principle, is an important element in evaluating it. So those who accept the Bible as the word of God may consider the ethical principles it states correct for that reason. There are, of course, other attitudes possible, as Socrates indicated in Plato's *Euthyphro* when he went through an elaborate discussion to conclude that the commands of God are not just simply because they are God's will, but rather that God can will only those things that are intrinsically just. In the following, I will not be much concerned with the ultimate origin of proposed goals but will treat them in their own right, as something to be considered on their merits.

Goals That Assume an Afterlife

The earliest type of general human goals that have been explicitly stated are closely connected with the idea that some aspect of the individual known as the soul survives the death of the body. If this premise is granted, then man's primary concern should be the welfare of his soul, if only because its duration will be so much longer than the life span of his body. Thinkers concerned with the welfare of the soul have often connected this with religious beliefs, by which I mean the existence of gods and their relation to man. The connection is, however, not logically necessary. It is, in fact, absent in the first known proposal of human goals connected with survival after death, that of Buddhism.

The earliest known Buddhist doctrines,[6] which may be a fair representation of the views of the founder of the religion, are straightforward. The Hindu doctrine of the Wheel of Life, or successive reincarnation of the soul into different identities after each death, is assumed. Memory of previous existences is considered vague but not entirely absent. There is no God in Buddhist doctrine who judges the soul after death. Nor is there anything like the Christian idea of heaven, although the Buddhist idea of the goal of human effort, called Nirvana, has often been confused with heaven.

The second important element in Buddhist doctrine is the idea that human life, and indeed all life as it is ordinarily lived, is basically a thing of pain and suffering. The argument for this view, at least in the early Buddhist writings, is that most men are subject to poverty and disease, and all men to age and death, and that these evils outweigh whatever good things are to be found in ordinary life. At the time that the Buddha lived, in 500 B.C., it was almost unimaginable that anything much could be done to eliminate these sources of human suffering. It may also be that the Buddha recognized that pain and suffering were basically symptoms of a deeper problem, that of human finitude. In any case he proposed to treat suffering on another level, through a change in attitude.

The goal announced by the Buddha was the elimination of human suffering. Since this could not be done directly, it would be done by making people care less about the things that involved suffering, that is, life in the world of the senses and the emotions, which Buddhists call sansara. The Buddha therefore preached a systematic detachment of the mind from any concern with the things of this world, which could bring it only sorrow. The mind that succeeded in losing all concern for these matters was said to have achieved Enlightenment or, in another phraseology, to have entered Nirvana.

Buddhist doctrines are purposely vague about precisely what this Enlightenment is. Its most important aspect is negative: the absence of the suffering caused by a concern with worldly matters. And this solution to the problem of suffering rests to a large extent on the belief in reincarnation, otherwise anyone who thought human life was thoroughly bad could eliminate his suffering by suicide. In the Buddhist doctrine, however, this would lead only to another life with equal suffering.

In the form that the Buddha himself seems to have taught it, which is now represented by the Theravada Buddhists, the elimination of suffering was a personal goal. In a short time, however, another branch of Buddhism arose, known as the Mahayana Buddhists, in which part of the duty of those who had progressed some way toward Enlightenment was to help their fellow men follow in their path.[7] One might say that the Theravada follow the Buddha's teachings and the Mahayana, his example. Since I am concerned here with group goals, I will consider the Mahayana approach. The goal the Mahayana Buddhists propose for humanity can be interpreted as mutual assistance in eliminating the individual suffering involved in the world of the senses by a systematic withdrawal of the mind from concern with it. The precise institutions through which people are to aid one another in attaining this withdrawal are another matter, and I will not assume here that the *institutions* of Mahayana Buddhism are part of the goal proposed or the best way of achieving it.

This version of Buddhism hardly seems a reasonable candidate for a long-range human goal today. There is no evidence to support the doctrine of successive reincarnation, and it would be very difficult if not impossible to make this consistent with the principle that all human functions are explicable through the known laws of physics. Furthermore, the idea that all human life is unavoidable suffering is not one that appears evident to modern man. Insofar as Buddha mentions specific things as examples of such suffering, the modern attitude would be that these can be eliminated by human effort. Therefore, I would conclude that the primitive Buddhism described here represents a cure for an imaginary disease.

Nevertheless, there may be modifications of this doctrine that are more relevant to our future goals. Detachment from the concerns of the sensory world could be made a goal in itself, independent of the rationale provided for it by primitive Buddhism, and justified on the ground that the introspective life of the mind is ultimately more satisfying than the life we usually lead. In this form, the goal would be shared by all who hold that individual mystic insight should be a primary human aim.

Alternatively, we could abstract from Buddhism the goal of eliminating individual suffering, without accepting the method proposed by the Buddhists for its accomplishment. This would require a precise statement of the causes and forms of suffering, since what makes one man suffer may be neutral or pleasant to another. If the root cause of mental suffering is the mind's recognition of its inability to accomplish all its desires, then the elimination of mental suffering may be very difficult.

The Buddhist approach would require us to give up caring about almost all the activities that usually concern us, and most men today would not accept this without some specific idea of what would remain for them. Unfortunately on precisely this matter, the nature of Enlightenment, Buddhist writings are most vague, and most Buddhist sources, both primitive and contemporary, reject the idea of ever understanding Enlightenment intellectually.[8] While this may not be a severe problem for those already committed to the quest, it is not a good way to convince those who are skeptical of it.

Other groups, notably the Christians and the Moslems, that have taken the immortality of the soul as a primary datum for determining human goals have set this view in a theological framework of ideas about the existence and nature of God. Most branches of these religions have believed that what happens to the soul after the death of the body depends on the details of the individual's life on earth, so that, for them, a major concern of life on earth is to ensure that the soul ends up well after death.[9]

Although the welfare of one's soul is an individual matter, both Christianity and Islam advocate an altruistic concern for the welfare of other men and maintain that an organized group—and ideally all of mankind—should cooperate in helping each man to live his life so that his soul will not be condemned in the afterlife. To be sure, the different versions of Christianity and Islam say different things about these matters, and much ink and blood have been spilt over them. The versions I am presenting seem to me to be in the mainstream of these religions, but I have not tried to find the most general areas of agreement.

According to these religions, what happens to the soul after death is determined by the extent to which it adhered to the moral precepts of God during its stay on earth.[10] Therefore, organized religious bodies have greatly stressed creating social conditions in which compliance with these principles was rewarded and violation of them punished. The theory behind this apparently is that men are often unable to recognize the value of following the moral injunctions by themselves, even though it is for their eventual good, and must therefore be externally coerced into doing so.

From this point of view, a long-range goal of

the human race would be the creation of conditions under which each man could live according to the ethical principles these religions take to be God's. Under these circumstances the salvation of the soul after death would presumably be assured.

The precise nature of the moral precepts to be followed is of less importance to us here than the religions' assumption that there must be some element of choice on the part of man as to whether he follows them. For example, it would not do to arrange human nature, through psychological conditioning or some similar method, so that men would have to act according to these principles, because this would not allow them the free choice between good and evil that is considered important. Therefore, the goals suggested by religions may have the additional feature of built-in restrictions on the methods permissible in accomplishing them. This occurs because these goals are really means to the otherworldly end of saving our souls.

To the extent that the principal motivation for following the moral precepts of a religion is to ensure that one's soul is well treated after death, the question of whether there really is a soul that survives death is foremost in deciding whether this is a goal worth pursuing. Let us therefore examine the evidence concerning this assumption, which must be considered as a statement about the world that can in principle be proven or disproven.

Direct evidence concerning the survival of the

soul would involve some contact between the living and the souls of the dead, which would presumably involve the influence of disembodied souls on ordinary matter, or conceivably a direct influence on the minds of living men. There are, of course, occasional reports of such contacts, under the name of ghosts, visions, etc. But while these reports cannot be dismissed out of hand, they do not have the character of reliable phenomena that can be studied as other natural phenomena are studied. It would therefore be dangerous to base the conclusion about so important a matter as survival after death upon this evidence. It is also my impression that few people regard such reports as the reason for their belief in the immortality of the soul.

I think the source of this belief is rather the feeling that man is the central element in the world, which was made for him. If this is the case, the idea that man's existence should be confined to the period of his physical life seems unreasonable, if only because it would be too much trouble to create a whole universe for a creature whose life is so short. This belief is reinforced by the further belief that man is qualitatively different from the rest of nature, and that the difference stems from his possession of an immortal soul.

While these ideas may have been reasonable before the development of modern science, they no longer seem to be so. This does not prove that such a soul cannot exist, but only that there is no evidence for it. If the soul did exist, there is no reason to expect that it would be as hard to detect in natural phenomena as it has been. An entity that supposedly plays such an important role in human life should give more evidence of itself. In the absence of evidence, it seems more reasonable to give up the hypothesis of the soul as an entity independent of the body, in which case it seems very unlikely that any aspect of the personality can survive the death of the body, although the possibility cannot be ruled out altogether. It would therefore appear that there is little evidence for the existence of a soul which can survive the death of the body.

The principles of modern science disprove the indirect arguments that in the past led to the belief in the soul. It would therefore appear that goals motivated by the idea of the existence of souls do not have any firm foundation in what we know about man and the world. I believe that the actions of most men, at least in the Western world, are in conformity with this conclusion, regardless of what people *say* about their belief in souls.[11]

Some religious men, particularly in the modern world, have implicitly recognized this and suggested that there are other reasons for following religious moral precepts. Some of them have maintained that these precepts are true, in the same sense that statements of mathematics or statements of physics can be true. If this were so, we would be making an error if we did not live by them. This view could perhaps be extended further to maintain that all of the long-range goals we are seeking are determined by objectively true moral principles.

I have indicated previously that the idea of an objective ethic, independent of human wishes, is not acceptable. Those who make a parallel between ethical statements and the statements of science are misled in several respects. The statements of ethics typically contain words like "should," and thus cannot be deduced from scientific statements, which do not contain this word or its synonyms. There is no source of evidence for ethical statements that corresponds to sense data for scientific statements, if one leaves out human preferences. Nor is there any comfort in the analogy between ethics and mathematics. The statements of mathematics are now understood to be analytic, that is, they do not give any information that is not contained in the assumptions made at the outset. So if ethical statements are analogous to mathematical ones, their truth depends entirely on our primitive assumptions, which are themselves ethical statements that must be justified on other grounds, so we are no closer to an objective ethics. Thus there appears to be no basis for the belief that the moral principles of religion are objectively true, or that any such objective moral principles, which can determine what our long-term goals should be, exist. This does not mean that ethical statements are meaningless. Individuals, societies, and perhaps all of mankind have ethical preferences and insofar as ethical statements reflect such subjective preferences, they are important and meaningful. We must, however, recognize them for what they are and not pretend that they have a greater force than their source would warrant.

One other justification sometimes given for following the moral principles of religion is that man has been specifically created by God to serve His ends, and therefore what human beings should do is learn God's will and fulfill it. What the will of God is may not be completely clear, but it is usually supposed to be at least partially revealed in the holy books, such as the Bible or the Koran.

I will not consider the moral aspects of choosing human goals according to the will of God, but merely observe that the view that man is a special creation is wholly at variance with scientific principles, which suggest that man is a continuous outgrowth of the rest of nature and that no cosmic plan is involved in his evolution.

Indeed, it is difficult to see how the existence of God can be maintained at all in the face of what we now know about the universe. The primitive idea, expressed, for example, in the Book of Job, that God is the agent causing natural phenomena that are not understood has become outmoded as the list of such phenomena has shrunk.[12] The later view of God as the planner and creator of the universe has also become obsolete with the recognition that the universe has no plan. The philosophical arguments for the existence of God, which seemed convincing to many medieval thinkers, are almost universally dismissed by modern philosophers as invalid.[13] I therefore think it time that scientists made clear to others that the hypothesis of God is unnecessary within the scientific picture of the world. Those men who wish to retain their belief in God anyway must recognize that none of the wide variety of phenomena revealed by the senses give any support to their belief.

The assertion that a particular way of life should be followed because it is God's will is therefore not convincing. This does not mean that the implied goal could not be accepted on other grounds. It does, however, imply that if we are looking for goals that can appeal to all of humanity, we should not consider those that depend upon God's existence for their motivation or accomplishment. Both for this reason, and because they are often based on such scientifically improbable assumptions as survival after death I am convinced that the specifically religious goals suggested by Christianity and Islam are not the proper goals of the human race. They do, however, express some important and persistent human dreams, and, when cast into a form consistent with the way the world is, they may become strong candidates for the goals we will choose.

One interesting effort in this direction has already been made by the Catholic paleontologist Teilhard de Chardin, most especially in his book *The Phenomenon of Man*.[14] Teilhard attempted to analyze man's past, present, and future in evolutionary terms but within the framework of Christian theology, that is, he assumed the existence of God and the immortality of the human soul. Teilhard was particularly concerned with the development of human consciousness out of unconscious matter. According to him, consciousness occurred in a primitive form in the first living creatures. As biologically more advanced organisms evolved, their level of consciousness increased. Indeed, for Teilhard, the evolution of consciousness was almost equivalent to biological evolution: "a consciousness is that much more perfected according as it lines a richer and better organized material edifice." This he called The Law of Complexity and Consciousness.

Teilhard's reinterpretation of evolution may or may not be an accurate statement about consciousness, but he did not stop there. He also considered the development of consciousness through the stages of mankind up to the present *Homo sapiens,* and through the distinct forms of human society. The emphasis here was on what he called collectivization, by which he meant that, through the process of forming societies and the resultant possibility of accumulating knowledge and other requisites of a rich mental life, a fusion of the consciousness of individual men is taking place into something greater, which he called the Spirit of the Earth.

It is tempting to interpret collectivization as another way of describing the facts with which we began this study, the approach to a single world society through improvement of communications, and the slow accumulation of human culture over the centuries. But to do this is purposefully to misunderstand Teilhard, who explicitly dis-

tinguished this process from what he called col-
lectivity.

It is difficult for me to understand precisely
what Teilhard meant by the union of selves into a
super consciousness. He apparently thought of
each man as possessing an individual soul distinct
from the matter comprising his body and believed that these souls joined with one another.
He gave no hint of a physical mechanism through
which the joining was accomplished, and this
presents a serious problem, since the human
mind, which is the highest form of consciousness
we know, requires a physical linkup between
brain cells. One could imagine such a physical
mechanism evolving between minds, but this
would presumably take a much longer time than
has been available in the development of human
societies.

I have a more important criticism of Teilhard's
ideas. The workings of evolution are not designed to reach some specific end like the unity
of all consciousness. The end point of evolution
may indeed involve such a unity, but it is not
built into the system. Nowhere in Teilhard's
considerations is there any indication of a role
for man's will in shaping his future evolution.
Instead, man is in the grip of the irresistible
force of natural evolution, which is leading him
to the next stage of complexity. This view has
been shared by other writers, notably George
Bernard Shaw, who talks of the Life Force, in
Man and Superman.[15]

Natural selection of random mutations, which produces biological evolution, is an incredibly slow process and cannot sensibly be said to influence what happens to one human generation, or even several hundred generations. It is hard to see what agent could be assumed to be directing the short-term collectivization Teilhard described, except the God Teilhard accepted. Therefore, Teilhard's view is tenable in the form he chose only under the assumption of God's existence. But in another form, it can be maintained even when this hypothesis is rejected; humanity might choose some sort of merged consciousness as one of its future goals. We could then start working toward this by whatever methods seem feasible for accomplishing it, rather than relying on the slow workings of biological evolution. Since I do regard this as an important candidate for a long-range goal of the human race, I will analyze its meaning and implications in greater depth later. At this point, I wish merely to express my admiration for Teilhard's clear intuition. Even though I think it is based on incorrect premises, I agree with his view of the eventual destiny of humanity. We differ mainly in that he sees man impelled toward that destiny for the outside, while I hope that we will make the free choice to go there.

The World Within the Mind

Another goal that has often been associated with the major world religions, although it is logically distinct from their teachings, is the achievement of mystic insight by individuals, which does not necessarily involve the assumption of a soul or the existence of God. Many men in many cultures have undergone and reported upon experiences of the type that are called mystic. A number of elements common to most of the experiences, which may therefore be taken to characterize them, have been analyzed in detail by William James in *The Varieties of Religious Experience*,[16] and by Walter T. Stace in *The Teachings of the Mystics*.[17] The common features these authors have noted include:

1. The apprehension of a unity between all aspects of the universe, sometimes called the oceanic feeling. Quite often there is also a feeling that one's own personality is merging into this cosmic unity.

2. A feeling that the experience itself cannot be described verbally or in terms of other experiences.

3. The strong conviction the experience conveys to those undergoing it, who commonly receive insights as vivid or more vivid than those of ordinary sense perception or intellectual analysis.

4. The positiveness of the experience, in the sense that it is associated with feelings of joy, peace, optimism, happiness, etc.

The similarity of the reports by people from many distinct backgrounds and circumstances indicate that the experiences involve something general about humanity, rather than something peculiar to certain cultures. This does not mean that the implications attached to the experience by those undergoing it are correct. These are usually religious in nature; for example, Christian mystics interpret the feeling of unity as a merging with God. Such interpretations, unlike the attributes of the experience itself, are not universal, but vary according to the background of the person. Hence there does not seem to be any reason to associate the mystic experience with religion per se, although it has certainly been the inspiration for much of the content of various religions.

A more central aspect of the interpretation of mystic experiences is the idea that they involve a contact between the mind and an objective aspect of reality that is distinct from the world revealed by sense impressions or intellectual processes. Such a claim, which is commonly made by those who have had these experiences, is strongly resisted by naturalistic thinkers, who have often been skeptical of the reports of the experiences themselves. I think this is somewhat unjustified. Phenomena that are sincerely reported by a wide variety of people have to be taken seriously however much they conflict with our deeply held beliefs. We should keep in mind Hamlet's injunction, "There are more things in heaven and earth, Horatio, than are dreamt of in your philosophy" (or, it might be added, physics).

The question of whether mystical experiences imply the existence of a different aspect of the world than that revealed by the senses is both a scientific and a linguistic one. It is scientific in the sense that scientists may try to account for mystic experiences in terms of the laws and objects that are found in the sensory world. It might be shown for example that a specific mystical experience is induced by a certain concentration of a particular chemical in the brain and never occurs otherwise. I think that the considerations discussed in Chapter II make it very plausible that something of this sort will indeed be proved. But this would not dispose of the mystics' claim that they have access to another world.

There is an analogy here to the phenomenon of vision. We know that vision depends on certain physiochemical changes in the retina of the eye, which take place whenever the sensation of seeing occurs in a person.[18] But the fact that seeing is dependent on chemical changes in the eye does not make the insight into the world that we obtain through visual experiences any less real, or deny the fact that we are learning something about the world that we could not obtain through our other senses. In the same way, although the experiences of mystics may be explicable in physical terms along with all other mental phenomena, this does not mean that they cannot provide us a different kind of insight into the one universe that exists than do the other experiences available to us. We must distinguish between understanding something by means of a complicated chain of logical reasoning coupled with sophisticated measurements, and understanding it by a simple interpretation of direct perceptions. The scientific explanation of the universe can presumably provide an understanding of the aspects of the world accessible to mystic experiences, but that understanding will have a different quality than one obtained by the direct experience, just as the picture of the astronomical universe we get by looking up on a starry night differs from the reconstruction of it we could make if we could not see ordinary light but detect it only with our instruments. The latter picture would obviously be much less rich and intuitive, even though it might contain the same information. So may it be with the scientific explanation of the mystic experience.

The insights obtained during mystic experiences cannot be accepted uncritically, however, particularly by those not having the experience. The very difficulty of communicating the content of such experiences must make us cautious about drawing general conclusions from them. Nevertheless, if we are to take the claims of the mystics seriously, we must face the decision of whether the mystic experience is something to be sought by all of humanity—a suggestion reinforced by the fact that the experience generally has a strongly positive character for those experiencing it, which is desirable independent of the intellectual value of the conclusions we draw from it.

Let us therefore consider as a potential long-range goal making the mystic experience available to all of humanity who wish it, rather than those few who seem to have achieved it thus far. Among the Western mystic writers, there is little hint of such a possibility for most people on earth, although it forms an important element of the Christian idea of heaven. On the other hand, it is the positive side of the goal of Mahayana Buddhism, whose negative side was discussed above, and it seems also to be the goal of the chemical mysticism of Timothy Leary and others who are spreading the news that mystic experiences can be induced at will by drugs such as LSD-25, and that these experiences are more desirable than ordinary experiences. In the classification system we have set up, this goal is basically divertive; it suggests that we concentrate on a type of activity not usually practiced by most men.

In suggesting the cultivation of mystical experiences as a goal, I am assuming there is a world of some depth to be explored there, some development to be found within those experiences, rather than a repetition of the same experience over and over again. If this is not the case, a single experience would be sufficient to exhaust the content of mysticism. But those who have had such experiences claim that the quality of the experiences becomes richer as the number increases. It would therefore perhaps be better to speak of the mystical life rather than of an individual experience as the long-range goal.

One of the difficulties with understanding the mystical life is why those who can have these experiences wish to come back from them to the sensory world at all. One possibility is that they have no control over the inception or termination of mystic experiences. If that is the case, one aspect of the goal could be to enable us to control the frequency and length of these experiences, for example by the use of drugs or electrical stimulation, once the physiological basis of mystic experiences is understood.

A further assumption of those sponsoring mysticism, or at least of the rhetoric usually written about mysticism, is that there is something external to ourselves being reached by the experience. I do not think this has been demonstrated by what is known about these experiences. The only indication that something objective is involved is the fairly universal agreement on their content, and this cannot be taken as a conclusive proof that the experience is not entirely in the mind. But why we are led to ascribe some experiences to an external world and not others is a difficult philosophical problem. Those experiences we call external seem to have two elements in common: they involve some degree of surprise, and they are not under the control of the mind. On both of these grounds, mystic experiences seem to indicate the existence of something external.

But perhaps the origin of the experiences is irrelevant to the acceptance of the mystic life for everyone as a long-range goal. For that purpose, it is the experience itself that is important. In a very important sense, all that matters to a man is what happens within his mind, and if the mystic experience is a new and valuable aspect of man's consciousness, he may consider it worth having even if it has no outside referent. If this should be the case, naturalist skeptics would be entitled to ask mystics to modify the language they use to describe their experiences, but not to renounce the experiences themselves.

A more relevant question is the extent to which the mystic life is consistent with other activities we might wish to carry out. The special state of consciousness involved does not seem to be well designed for the kind of understanding involved in the ordinary intellectual process. Hence a man who decides to pursue mystical experiences may have to renounce this other kind of understanding. If the human race as a group chose this, it might well be impossible simultaneously to pursue the goal of understanding the sensory world. It might also prove very difficult to enjoy the pleasures of ordinary life, although opinions among the mystics differ on this. There is certainly a strong ascetic strain among mystics that points in this direction, but the contemporary chemical mystics claim that sensory pleasures are heightened while the mystical experience is taking place. So it may be that by suitable methods we can have the best of both worlds.

In balance, I believe that we need more information about the mystic experience to make a rational decision about pursuing it as a general goal. Since it involves a different kind of consciousness, a better understanding of consciousness in general would be relevant. It is also important to know whether mystic experiences can be induced and prolonged at will, perhaps with the aid of chemical agents, since these agents might be able to affect the quality of the experiences, perhaps to produce a different type than occurs "naturally." Finally, although it is not logically necessary for the purpose of deciding about mysticism as a goal, it would be very interesting to understand more about whether there is anything outside of our minds to which the mystic experience is referring.

Unlike most of the goals proposed in the past, that of achieving mystic experiences may not contradict the scientific world view. It remains to be seen whether it is sufficiently appealing to people to be taken seriously as a long-range human goal.

Individualism Reconsidered

Individualism, the view that it should be the aim of human society to enable its members to pursue their own individual purposes as freely as possible,[19] has generally been implicit rather than explicit for those who have favored it. The assumption is that human beings are so different that it is neither desirable nor feasible to find group goals that might appeal to all of us. Each man is the best judge of his own happiness and what will contribute to it, and the most society can do is make it easy for him to attain this and at the same time interfere as little as possible with a similar pursuit by others.

I think there are two valid reasons for calling this a long-range human goal. First, this condition is obviously not satisfied anywhere on earth today. Second, it involves certain presuppositions

about human beings that are probably not yet
valid, so that some reconstruction of man as well
as of society may be required if it is to be attained. It would come under the heading of developmental, individual goals.

The idea of constructing a society in which
human beings would be more free to follow their
individual dictates has been a very beneficial one
in the past, particularly in the eighteenth and
nineteenth centuries, when it led to a major
change in human outlook.[20] It would, however,
be unwise to conclude that this is the only aim
of society without exploring alternative possibilities and examining some of the implications of
restricting our goals to total individualism.

One important presupposition of this goal is
that men are agents with free wills and innate
desires and purposes independent of social conditioning. This picture of man is a very old one,
going back at least as far as Socrates,[21] and it
appears to be implicitly based on the notion that
men have souls, which are set at birth and relatively uninfluenced by upbringing. If this were
so, efforts to reshape men by psychological conditioning would be not only futile, but immoral,
and a natural goal would be a society in which
men were most free to act according to their innate individual wills.

The discoveries of both psychology and an-
thropology as well as the common sense of everyday life challenge the notion that each man is
set at birth with an unalterable disposition to
wish certain things. The study of different cul-

tures has shown that some of the things most highly desired by individuals in one culture, such as the accumulation of possessions, may be of little interest to people brought up in another.[22] Even such supposedly fundamental drives as having children vary significantly with the social situation; this drive was effectively repressed in the upper classes in Imperial Rome,[23] and is today in many classes in eastern Europe.[24] An individual's likes and dislikes are strongly influenced by what he was exposed to in his childhood, and by the groups with which he associates in his daily life. It is unlikely, for instance, that the recent preference of teenagers for the sound of the Beatles over that of Lawrence Welk was an expression of the innate feelings of several million people. The experience of the advertising industry is a testimony to the possibility of molding human preferences by outside influences.

It is still possible to consider the goal of total individualism, even after recognizing that society and upbringing play a crucial role in determining what one's preferences will be. But there would seem to be something incomplete in constructing a society in which everyone is free to act upon his desires without paying attention to how these desires are influenced by the society itself. This does not mean that we should go to the opposite extreme and try to create a society that consciously predetermines the desires of individuals; this would put an unjustifiable reliance on our understanding of what is best for people. We should not, however, feel any qualms about introducing ethical principles for determining human actions other than the arbitrary preferences that the people alive at one time have for running their own lives. In other words, while total individualism may be one long-range human goal, I do not think it should be the only one.

The goal of total individualism by itself also presupposes either that human nature and the human condition are relatively fixed, or that there is little need to make any improvement in them. In this sense, its proponents are relatively complacent about human life. They believe that if the restrictions on freedom of action imposed by society and the environment were eliminated, life would become much better than it is now for most people. One may agree with this without accepting the further conclusion that this is the best humanity could do for itself, and that none of our problems arises from the way we are, rather than from the restrictions of the environment.

There are at present some societies, such as Sweden, where the goal of total individualism is at least approached, and there is much to recommend the kind of life available in these places. But it does not seem to me that the people living under these conditions are significantly better off than the rest of us in regard to the negative aspects of the human condition. In fact, members of such groups seem particularly prone to feel a lack of purpose in their lives, which might indeed be expected in a society that disregards the sources of human motivation. It is quite likely that when the problems of daily life, which have historically been the major concern of most men, are lifted the feeling of a lack of purpose will be a very common reaction unless we devote considerable care to the methods by which people are motivated.

Motivation presents another problem as well. It is usually assumed that in a society where everyone is free to follow his individual interests, there will be a sufficient number who choose to work at such things as art or scientific research. I consider this an unwise assumption with no strong evidence to support it among the groups that seem to be freest of arbitrary restrictions by society, such as those with inherited wealth. Therefore, if the proponents of total individualism wish to guarantee that such activities continue, they will have to motivate people to do them. Since one source of motivation could be the accomplishment of other long-range human goals, this again suggests that total individualism makes sense only as one of several such goals.

There is one other point to be made about the goal of a society in which everyone has maximum freedom to fulfill his individual desires. In spite of the claims sometimes made that society is becoming more repressive of the individual, I think there are indications that we are moving in the direction of more freedom. The progress we are making is somewhat obscured by the fact that as the number of people increases and society becomes more complex, it becomes more difficult to harmonize the desires of different people when these conflict. Since it is inherent in the goal that each man's wishes are equally important, this can lead to situations in which no one can do what he really wants to. It is therefore possible that in a complex society devoted to total individualism, there might be less freedom in some respects than in a simpler society that did not consciously accept this principle. If so, it would be important to investigate how societies could be reorganized to minimize conflicts between the wishes of individuals, if total individualism were adopted.

The goal of total individualism raises many questions that can be answered only by going beyond the goal. The most difficult is probably the sources of motivation for the activities that people will be free to carry out. If the framers of the society disregard these, there will be an irresistible temptation to control the society by manipulating motivations, and the freedom will be largely a sham. In spite of the problems connected with it, the goal is surely an attractive one to modern man, and it will doubtlessly receive a good deal of support when the choice of goals is being made. It would therefore be helpful if those sponsoring it considered it from the point of view of malleable human nature, rather than of atomic units with fixed preferences. The new insights obtained in this way might indicate what other long-range goals would harmonize with total individualism.

Indefinite Progress and the Perfectibility of Man

The eighteenth-century philosophers were responsible for the expression of the goal of total individualism and, indirectly, for the origin of societies that represented a step in that direction. Some of these philosophers also proposed another long-range goal, although, characteristically, they stated it as a necessity rather than a free choice. This was the goal of continual progress in human capabilities through the growth of science, technology, and other disciplines that have a cumulative structure. Condorcet's doctrine of the "indefinite perfectibility of man" was the purest statement of the idea that progress toward the betterment of human faculties would continue into the indefinite future, having been held back until then only by superstition and ignorance.

Condorcet's ideas are given in an abbreviated form in his *Sketch for a Historical Picture of the Progress of the Human Mind*.[25] This begins with mankind in the tribal stage and traces knowledge and culture through various societies up to the French Revolution, when the book was written. Condorcet then goes on to consider the future development of the human mind and in the last section of the book declares his views on human perfectibility.[26] He predicts that in the future there will be increased equality among nations, and among men within a nation, both of which we have seen come to pass in the two centuries since he wrote. He also predicts the tremendous improvement in the standard of living that has occurred, and, anticipating Malthus, suggests that this may eventually be threatened by an increase in population, to which he also anticipates the "modern" solution, that is, birth control.

Most of Condorcet's analysis deals with the development of the human mind and knowledge within the framework of existing human biology. But here too he makes some remarks that suggest the present view that human biology itself may be modified. In particular, he says that the progress of medicine may increase the life span indefinitely, and even indicates some ideas of biological evolution. Condorcet was a good deal ahead of his time and perhaps more optimistic about the future than any writer until the present. His attitude is not an uncommon one among contemporary scientists, and the main intellectual objection I see to it is that it seems doubtful to me that this progress will continue naturally into the indefinite future without human planning to assist it.

The Enlightenment philosophers recognized that progress would occur only in some kinds of societies and therefore maintained that the form of society should be one in which progress would occur. Since they thought of the barriers to progress as negative factors in society, such as suppression of free thought by religion, their main emphasis was on the removal of these barriers. Although there were occasional suggestions about the creation of positive institutions that would increase the rate of progress, the prevailing attitude was that progress was inherent in man's nature, providing no efforts were made to repress it.[27]

This view was given what appeared to be a firmer theoretical basis in the nineteenth century with the discovery of biological evolution. Since evolution contained a mechanism for inducing a progression from less well to better adapted organisms, it seemed reasonable to such philosophers as Herbert Spencer[28] that this progression would also occur automatically in man, leading to the perfectibility described by Condorcet. The important thing was to allow the workings of evolution through a proper choice of social system because genetic natural selection, the method of biological evolution, is too slow to have much effect in human history. As a result, Spencer emphasized the importance of insuring that those naturally fittest to survive were not disfavored by the workings of the social system in comparison with the unfit. Even Darwin to some extent shared this view, which has at times been used to protest the use of medical treatment to preserve the lives of people with diseases like diabetes, on the ground that this allows them to reproduce themselves and thus interferes with the workings of evolution to eliminate the disease.

One intellectual problem connected with the evolutionary approach to indefinite progress is that there is no indication of the time scale for such progress. It may be of little comfort to know that the ills that afflict men now will be cured in some indefinite future. Also, in the view of the believers in the evolutionary scheme, progress is automatic if man does not interfere with its workings. But many men wish to have a hand in making progress, if only by helping it occur faster. The nineteenth-century version of human evolution left little scope for this, and indeed suggested that human interference was more likely to hinder than to help progress. These objections would not necessarily be important if progress through evolution were really automatic. But there is reason to doubt this.

This rests partly on the definition of progress. Even if there is a mechanism that aids the survival of the fittest in human societies, fitness is a relative concept, which itself depends on the society. In a society that emphasized war, aggressiveness would be a useful quality, whereas in one that avoided war, it might be contra-survival. In biological evolution, the natural environment defines fitness by whether or not the organism can survive. The fittest are by definition the ones that survive to have the most offspring. In the human context, we call a development progressive only if it agrees with some notion we have of going from bad to good, or from good to better. There is little reason to expect that there is any mechanism in human affairs that will guarantee the occurrence of such developments in the long run, without our conscious efforts to bring them about. To believe otherwise seems like an attempt to bring back the notion of divine providence in another guise.

In the twentieth century there have been further attempts to discover a parallel to biological evolution in the cultural development of humanity,[29] and there are indeed a number of striking analogies between the two processes, particularly if we represent culture by the level of technology. In most cases a higher level of technology represents a survival factor for a human group and is therefore likely to enable them to propagate their culture more successfully than their competitors. There is also a clear analogy between the information-carrying ability of the genes that enables favorable characteristics to be passed on to new generations and the use of language by human beings to pass on cultural information. The progressive nature of at least the technological aspect of culture can be reasonably explained by such factors.

Again, however, the problem of the meaning of "progress" arises. Some critics have suggested that the added technological competence that enabled first western Europe and then the United States to spread their versions of culture was not progress at all, and that some of the cultures that have unsuccessfully competed with the West, for example the Polynesian, might have been more desirable models for human society. A case might be made for this, but what the suggestion really proves is that even if there is a progressive evolutionary aspect to the development of human culture, there is no objective reason for us to accept it as good. Therefore, I do not believe that this progression defines the way we should necessarily choose to go. Rather, if we can isolate the elements in human life that lead to the evolutionary aspects of cultural development, we can use them to direct our future development in the path that we choose for it to take.

One way to make the notion of progress more precise would be to consider our potentialities rather than what we actually do. At any given time in human history, there are some things that we as a group can imagine as possible, but cannot yet accomplish. It is easiest to describe these things in science and technology, but they are also present in other fields, such as athletics. We might define as a part of progress any development that enables us to accomplish something we could not do before, whether or not we choose to do it in practice.

It is this aspect of progress that has best characterized the contribution of the West, and particularly the United States, to the world in the past three centuries. If we were to consider as a goal the indefinite extension of such progress, there are at least two questions to be answered: is indefinite progress of this type really possible, and why is it desirable?

On the question of possibility, while the laws of nature may put general limits on human accomplishments, we are very far from having reached any of them yet. Although the laws of physics, for instance, imply that certain phenomena cannot occur, these phenomena are generally rather abstract, and the fact that they cannot occur does not suggest that we cannot do the things we are likely to be interested in. For example, the conservation of energy implies that we cannot do useful work without some external source of energy. This, however, is no problem as long as plentiful sources of such energy are available. We may have to go to some lengths to obtain it, such as learning to utilize thermonuclear reactions, but this does not seem to be forbidden by any physical laws. Even travel to the stars, which is made very difficult by the limiting velocity of light, cannot be said to be impossible on that account. If the human life span could be increased to ten thousand years, then travel to the nearest stars could be accomplished without exorbitant energy expenditure well within a lifetime.

There are many approaches that can be taken toward the accomplishment of any given endeavor, and I do not think it wise ever to believe that there is no approach that will work, at least for the things we can now imagine. Therefore, if the human race were to choose as a goal the systematic extension of our capabilities for such accomplishment, I do not think we could be demonstrably shown to have made a scientific error.

This is probably the case even for those activities that are closely linked to man's basic biology and psychology. If there is something we cannot accomplish because of the way man now is, we can imagine changing how he is in order to make it possible. Thus if man cannot survive long space voyages because of psychological problems such as loneliness, or because of biological problems such as loss of strength under zero gravity conditions, we can imagine producing alterations in at least some men so as to eliminate these problems for them. While this runs some danger of destroying the unity of humanity that has been so laboriously achieved, I believe it is mainly a matter of attitude, and that a man is anything we call one.

The goal of indefinite progress would be a Faustian goal in my terminology, since it does not have any definite end in sight. Part of the rationale for wanting indefinite progress is the hope that some of the activities that this will make possible will be good things in comparison to what we now have. Another rationale is that the new forms of man that come about through such progress may have a qualitatively different outlook on the world than we do, and therefore not suffer from some of the ills of the present human condition. Of course, they may have troubles of their own.

Another virtue of indefinite progress as a goal is that there seems to be a real human need to try to accomplish what we cannot yet do. The very idea that we are engaging in an effort to overcome our present limitations will be a solace to some of us. If we can become convinced that the future will see the fulfillment of anything that mankind can imagine, it may seem more bearable that there are many dreams that cannot now be fulfilled. At least many men have expressed such an attitude for their personal lives.

Indefinite progress has many virtues as a long-term goal, but it also has several drawbacks, which I believe make it unsatisfactory as a single goal and, to some extent, as part of a set of goals. While we may be able to accomplish anything we choose, we cannot accomplish everything. There are many lines of development that can be pursued to overcome our limitations, and if we enter upon one of them, it is quite likely that we will foreclose the pursuit of several others. As a result, we will make progress, but not the same progress we would have made by following another path, and I see no reason to expect that all paths lead to the same final state.

This is another aspect of the problem we noted in Chapter III in connection with possible coming developments in technology. So long as our progress is not applied to our lives, there may not be much interference with other possible developments. But once we choose to realize one of the possibilities we have developed, this is not likely to remain true. If effective aging control became possible, and the human life span became several thousand years, it would then be possible to explore other stellar systems by sending spaceships there. However, it is also possible that, given a much longer life span, men would be less willing to risk themselves in dangerous activities such as space travel. In that case interstellar travel would become psychologically unfeasible at the very time it became technically feasible. This would mean the blocking of a road we might otherwise have taken, say by the use of drugs or low temperatures to decrease the metabolism of interstellar travelers enough so that they could reach the stars without an increased life span.

It is not that this development would be intrinsically good or bad, but rather that it illustrates the strong possibility that going in one direction may make it difficult to reach the same point as going in another. Therefore, if we choose to follow the route of indefinite progress, we seem to have two alternatives. One would be to refrain from putting into practice, except perhaps on a very small scale, any of the possibilities that our progress leads us to. In my opinion, this would require more forbearance than men are capable of. It would also make the whole idea of progress academic and perhaps uninteresting. The other alternative would be to have some way of choosing which of the possible directions of progress we wish to take. But this is exactly what our long-range goals are supposed to help us determine. Therefore, indefinite progress is not a goal at all but rather an aspect of the life of mankind, which our goals will help us to channel properly. While we might choose either to renounce such progress or to cultivate it, this decision is secondary to the decision on what we want to accomplish in the long run.

The philosophers who conceived of indefinite progress did us the valuable service of pointing out that we need not accept any external limitations on what we will become. However, if mankind remains united we *will* become only a few of the many hypothetical things we might become. There is no single direction for progress, and the final choice remains for us to make. After we have, we can embark on some of the many paths available to us. Very possibly we will want to explore some side directions as well as the main paths, on the chance that some of the benefits of a Faustian search will be gained in this way. Thus Condorcet's marvelous vision is only a part of the truth; it specifies a voyage man is making, but does not identify the reason for the trip, or how the course is plotted.

It is obviously impossible to make an exhaustive survey of all the goals that have been proposed in the past, so I will rest my case here. I feel reasonably confident that my conclusions about the inadequacy of the goals we have considered here would be confirmed by a more searching analysis. If, however, I am mistaken and humanity chooses to adopt one or more of the goals I have rejected, it will still be a step in the right direction. As the reader must have realized, I am more convinced of the need for goals than of the virtue or lack of it in any particular goal.

The goals I have rejected here either made invalid assumptions about the natural world, or involved incomplete analyses of human motivations and requirements, and it may legitimately be asked whether any conceivable goal can withstand this type of critical analysis. In the following section, I suggest one such goal. The reader may decide for himself whether I am correct.

A POSSIBLE GOAL—THE EXTENSION OF CONSCIOUSNESS

The philosopher Democritus once said that "in reality there are only atoms and the void."[30] And as we have seen, modern science has substantiated that all phenomena of the natural world can be understood in terms of the behavior of atomic particles moving through space. For a short time in the history of the earth, something has, however, existed that, although it may have an explanation in the properties of matter in motion, could not easily have been foreseen. This is the phenomenon we call consciousness. So far as we know, consciousness is a very new development, associated with only a small part of the material world. There is no indication that consciousness extends beyond the higher animals, and where it exists, it is a fragile thing, dependent on the proper functioning of countless biophysical processes, which are themselves too primitive and widespread in nature to be an aspect of consciousness. This dependence of mind on matter is aptly summed up in the phrase "to think, we must eat."[31] Even the central role of consciousness in the psychic life of man has been questioned by the psychoanalysts, who say that much of what we think and do is determined by parts of our mind that are ordinarily inaccessible to our consciousness.

From another point of view, consciousness has a unique role in the world. In its absence, natural phenomena would be like a play with no audience. The phenomena would take place in the same way, but no one would know or care. Such a world seems impoverished in comparison to ours, in which, through the existence of conscious beings, matter has begun to be aware of its own secrets.

Whatever the overall role of consciousness is in the universe, to an individual man, his own consciousness is an important and a precious thing. It is therefore surprising that the investigations of scientists and philosophers have produced few clear insights about its nature. Perhaps the nature of consciousness is one of the things about which it is difficult to communicate one's insights to someone else. I will assume, in describing the goal of the extension of consciousness to higher forms than now exist, that we each have some intuitive grasp of what consciousness means. The aspects of consciousness relevant to its extension will emerge as we go along.

Levels of Consciousness

In spite of the difficulty in comparing the consciousness of two different minds, it is frequently possible to say that one is higher than another. Few people would doubt that human beings display a higher development of consciousness than ants, or even chimpanzees, or that the consciousness of adult humans is at a higher level than that of infants. In making these judgments, we are using the external manifestations of consciousness, since we have no way of getting inside the mind of anyone else. But no one except convinced solipsists will object to the use of behavior to measure the level of consciousness.

It does not seem useful to distinguish levels of consciousness in normal adult human beings, since the differences in behavior among them are not very great in comparison to the differences between humans and other species. We can, however, imagine criteria that could be used to say that some entity possessed a higher form of consciousness than adult human beings. These criteria might be qualitative, in that they would involve new forms of behavior as manifestations of the higher form of mind. Or they could be quantitative, in the sense that the conscious entity would involve a combination of several already conscious beings into some merged form.

The cultural development of mankind, at least since the development of writing, has not, it seems to me, resulted in a qualitatively higher form of consciousness. The contents of our consciousness have changed considerably over a much shorter period, but it is likely that the conscious experience now is similar to what it was in Sumer, five thousand years ago. The thoughts expressed by men over the years have a similar tone and form to thoughts expressed by men today. And if the written expression of the thoughts is similar, we may expect that the inner experiences were similar also. After all, it is on the basis of the expression of thoughts that we attribute consciousness to other beings.

One sign of a new form of consciousness, in man or elsewhere, would be evidence of control by the mind of a wider class of mental activities, for example, a direct control by the mind over the creative processes that are now generally unconscious. Another would be the ability to make conscious the sometime unconscious motivations of our actions. In each of these cases, it would be the capability to explain to others what was going on in these hidden areas that would be taken as evidence of the new abilities. The major difference would, however, be internal feeling, not external behavior.

A higher level of consciousness might also involve the attainment at will of states of consciousness of a qualitatively new kind, like the mystic experience, and the integration of their contents with those of other experiences in a way not yet achieved. These new states of consciousness would not necessarily involve the "oceanic" feeling reported by mystics; they could be any new states of mind whose attainment is under control, but I think it crucial that they be able to be integrated with other experiences. Otherwise madmen would be candidates for a higher consciousness. We want to improve on what we have now, which means that we must retain what we have and add to it. Such qualitative changes in consciousness have occurred in the past. The first use of verbal thinking by human beings is one example, and there were probably earlier ones as well.

A change in consciousness might also result from replacing one form of mental activity by another, more direct one. At present the perception of color or position is direct and intuitive for us, while the recognition of logical or mathematical relationships among ideas is indirect and usually the result of a long series of intermediate steps. It is conceivable that other minds—perhaps some form of artificial intelligence we will one day create—might see these relationships much more directly than we do, and for such minds, the understanding of natural phenomena would be as effortless as counting stones is for us. Minds that could perceive relations directly in this way, whatever their origin, would, if they kept our other abilities, be a step toward a higher level of consciousness than ours.

Other qualitative changes in consciousness that may be possible probably cannot now be imagined by us for want of a model. The examples given here should serve to illustrate that it is unlikely that the human mind as it presently exists is the highest conceivable form of consciousness.

Quantitative advances in consciousness are also possible. The most obvious would be some sort of shared consciousness among several minds, human or otherwise. This suggests something like mental telepathy, or awareness of another person's thought, but I mean something more thoroughgoing. Many writers have imagined telepathy as a kind of soundless speech between minds that remain distinct entities; what I imagine is perhaps a temporary fusing of the two minds into one, with no more feeling of separateness than now exists in the mind of one person. This is to be contrasted with the sense of being an observer of something outside one's own consciousness which is what happens now when we communicate with another person.

Such a merger of consciousnesses would presumably have to involve some kind of physical link between the brains involved and could occur either among several human minds, or, if we create artificial intelligence or meet other intelligent species, could involve these as well. If it can be achieved at all, it can perhaps be extended to include as many individual minds as desired. But that remains to be seen.

An obvious question is whether the individual minds retain their own consciousness while merged into the greater consciousness. In the absence of any experience, I would guess that if there were really a merging of minds, there would be no sense of individual consciousness. In fact, I would tend to use this as one criterion for the success of the merger. One of the hallmarks of consciousness is the sense of unity among all phenomena in the mind, and I think this sense would tend to overwhelm any residual feeling of separateness after the merged consciousness had existed for a while. It may be significant that the two halves of the human brain do not seem to be individually conscious in the normal human being, although it is possible to

make them so by severing the connections between them.[32] In this case something about the
linkup apparently supersedes the feeling of individual consciousness, so we may perhaps conclude that consciousness identifies itself with the
limit of its scope.

The first attempts at merged consciousness
would probably be temporary; after a time the
individual minds would separate and work independently again. This would give them a chance
to see whether they preferred individuality or the
merged state. Eventually, a group of minds might
choose to remain permanently united, thus creating a new being.

It seems likely that such a merged consciousness would have some of the new qualitative features I have described above, in addition to the
sum of the minds of its constituents. Certainly
human consciousness has qualities going beyond
those of the individual neurons, or even those of
individual sections of the brain. And since many
human beings prize consciousness above all
things, and do not willingly restrict its scope in
themselves, it is plausible to guess that beings
possessing a higher form of consciousness would
also find it good and would wish to keep it.

As I have suggested, something that could be
said to have a higher form of consciousness than
ours may already exist in other parts of the universe, or may someday be created on earth artificially without the participation of the human
mind. Science fiction writers have given some
fairly graphic descriptions along both of these

lines.[33] Neither of these possibilities would be directly relevant to human goals, but both would touch on them indirectly. A machine consciousness could provide a model for some innovations we might want to make in human consciousness, as well as being a possible partner for men in the merging of minds. The criterion for consciousness in a machine is a more complicated question than the criterion for intelligence, but it is probably not really different in kind from the criteria we use for recognizing that other human beings are conscious; we would have to judge from the machine's behavior that something inside was controlling its activities. Conscious machines will almost certainly be appreciably more difficult to construct than intelligent machines. Research along these lines, however, would be an indispensable aid in learning how to extend consciousness.

Extraterrestrial consciousness would touch on human goals if we might someday wish to go beyond the human race alone and consider the common goals of all conscious creatures. The same logic that leads to the conclusion that humanity is one brotherhood will, I believe, eventually lead to the same conclusion about all forms of consciousness in the universe. When this is recognized we will be driven to ask about the common goals of the commonwealth of conscious beings. In the absence of any knowledge of what the commonwealth contains it is impossible to discuss these in detail. Yet surely goals of a group of entities that have only consciousness in common would also relate to consciousness. Indeed, the extension of consciousness may be the long-term goal of all creatures that possess it.

The Value of Extending Consciousness

I have argued that the root of man's discontent is his finitude and inability to accomplish all that he wills. To some extent this problem must exist for any conscious creature, since it is a consequence of the separation between the mind and the world. If we wish to attack the source of human unhappiness, we must do something about this conflict. One possibility would be to eliminate consciousness, but this would leave the world very much the poorer, and most of us are too attached to the mind to abolish it. The alternative is to extend the scope of consciousness in such a way as to lessen, and eventually remove, the discrepancy between will and achievement.

There are many ways to extend the domain of our consciousness. We can increase the control we have over the external world through our technology. This path has been and will continue to be very important to man. But this cannot be the complete answer. There is a qualitative difference between our conscious control over our mental activities and our influence on the outside world. What we would like to do is to bring more of the totality of experience into the direct control of our consciousness, that is, to internalize more of the outside world.

This may seem strange in view of the sharp

distinction generally made between the two. Yet to one person, the mind of another person, to the extent that it is accessible at all through perceptions, is part of the outside world. If a merger of consciousnesses of the type described above could be attained, the minds would both be a part of the consciousness of one being. Similarly, the extension of the range of our consciousness to include parts of our mental activities now unconscious would be such an internalization of something we do not now control consciously. In both of these cases, the domain of consciousness would be spread to include mental phenomena external to individual consciousness. This would be a step toward the elimination of the conflict between one mind and the world outside, but not the end of it; consciousness would still have to be extended to realms not considered mental at all.

The achievement of new levels of consciousness would not only internalize part of the outside world, but presumably also change the internal world qualitatively. And just as it is difficult for us to imagine our minds as they would be if they were diminished in any way, so it is difficult to imagine them qualitatively augmented, or to conceive how it would feel to occupy the next stage in consciousness. A remarkable series of efforts to do this appear in the novels of Olaf Stapledon,[34] particularly *Odd John, Last and First Men, Death into Life,* and *The Star Maker.* But even these deeply felt attempts are somewhat like a blind man's descriptions of color to another blind man.

Perhaps when those with higher consciousness are created or developed, they will be able to give us some feeling of the new levels on which they operate. But mystics' lack of success in communicating their experiences does not augur well for the possibility of our understanding beings who are permanently on this level. We must wait to see. If we cannot understand, we will have to take their word for how it feels.

In spite of the difficulty of imagining how superconscious men would feel, these feelings must enter into our wish to extend consciousness. Whatever the ultimate end of such a process of extension, I do not think that we would willingly condemn whole generations and orders of beings to misery in order to fulfill the end. We need some conviction that any change in the level of consciousness will produce beings that are not more discontent with their fates than we are. The belief that consciousness is the best thing we know of in the universe and that we are acting to improve upon it may give us the conviction that what we do to extend consciousness is good, but it cannot ensure that the products will feel the same way.

If they do not, they will be free to try to make something better. Because of the inner logic of the conflict between the unity of one consciousness and the diversity of phenomena in the external world, there is probably no level of consciousness in which the conscious being will rest content until the sway of consciousness is extended indefinitely. Therefore, although there are persuasive reasons for trying to produce forms of consciousness higher than our own, this is best regarded as merely one step by consciousness in its effort to gain complete dominance over the world. It is the furthering of this process that I consider to be a natural goal for humanity, and in fact for all conscious creatures, be they humans, Martians, dolphins, or IBM 137000. Let us then consider what is implied by the ultimate extension of consciousness, and how we might go about proceeding toward it.

The Ultimate Range of Consciousness

Consciousness has evolved in the history of the earth from its beginnings in simpler forms of life to its present highest state in the human mind. Possibly a similar process has gone further in other parts of the universe. Yet in any form in which it presently exists, consciousness is severely limited in its scope. It is limited in time, since the individual human mind has a beginning and an end. It is limited in its powers by the intransigence of the external world to its will. It is limited in its occurrence to a very small part of the world of matter. Finally, there is not one consciousness but many, and these are so completely separated from one another that communication between them is a pale shadow of the unity within a single mind.

The road to the elimination of these limitations will be a long one, and its end is not really conceivable to us. Nevertheless, we can try to understand some of the circumstances involved in the ultimate extension of consciousness. Both Olaf Stapledon and Teilhard de Chardin have written about this, and their remarks are similar to the ones I will make here.

In order to overcome its limitations, consciousness would have to transform itself into a single, universal entity; it would have to become associated with all forms of matter that occur in the world, not just the special organic molecules found in the brain, and the many isolated minds that do not share the sense of unity that defines a single consciousness would not exist. The ultimate range of consciousness would be, essentially, a conscious universe, each part of which plays a role in the overall consciousness and no part of which is regarded as the external world by that consciousness. A poet might say that consciousness must become coextensive with creation.

Such a universal consciousness would be no more finite than the universe itself. What limitations it had would come only from the laws of nature, and these would define it rather than limit it. We are most often unhappy over not what we are, but things outside of us that interfere with our will. There would be nothing outside the universal consciousness, and so this source of unhappiness would be eliminated.

Since the human mind is usually conscious of something outside of itself, one may wonder what the universal consciousness would be conscious of. The answer, of course, is aspects of itself. While consciousness is unified, all of its aspects do not occur simultaneously. We are sometimes conscious of sensations coming from the outside, at other times of our own memories or thoughts. But even if there were no outside for us, in the sense that everything were under our conscious control, there could still be a change in the content of our mind with inner time, and the totality of these contents would be what we were conscious of. In other words, the complete internalization of the external world would not eliminate the objects of consciousness; it would simply mean that all of these objects would be under the control of the consciousness, instead of only some of them as at present.

We can do no more here than define the universal consciousness. To imagine the quality of its life is beyond us. It would not suffer the ills that beset our finite consciousness and would be capable of realms of achievement at which we cannot even guess. In the most far-seeing of his novels, *The Star Maker,* Stapledon discusses such a consciousness, which he calls the Cosmical Spirit. He suggests that it may experience discontent in connection with its having been created with definite form and potentiality, rather than being eternal and unlimited. But Stapledon does not consider the Cosmical Spirit the highest form of consciousness; it is subordinate to its creator, whom Stapledon calls the Star Maker. If there is no Star Maker, then the universal consciousness need not feel any shame about its inadequacies, since there will be nothing to which it can compare itself unfavorably.

Those who believe in God may try to identify the universal consciousness with Him, and argue that He already exists, so there is no need to create Him. As I have mentioned, there does not appear to be evidence for this. Furthermore, a crucial aspect of the universal consciousness as I conceive it is that it should be a unity of all consciousness. Even if God does exist, other consciousness obviously also exists, which is not integrated into a universal consciousness. Therefore the existence of God is irrelevant to the question of producing the universal consciousness that will unite all finite minds.

The goal I propose for humanity is the creation of a universal consciousness. This must be voluntary on the part of mankind, and it will eventually require the participation, in the deepest sense, of all men. Indeed, in order to create a universal mind, all conscious beings in the universe, from the simplest to the most advanced, must participate. Thus this should really be considered a goal for all conscious creatures, rather than just for the human race. Although we may initiate the goal, and take the first steps toward it, if it is to be accomplished we will eventually have to cooperate with other intelligent beings.

When consciousness becomes a universal attribute, then it can at last play the role to which it is entitled by the value we put upon it. What will happen after that can hardly be determined here. The universe will have become something quite different from what it now is, and perhaps even the laws of nature will not retain their present form. Our own role as individuals and as a race will have been carried out, and I think we can reasonably leave it to our successors to ponder upon the further evolution of a conscious universe.

The creation of a universal consciousness is as long-term a goal as anything we can imagine. It is a final goal for the human race, since upon its accomplishment the human race will have become a part of something greater. But in spite of the fact that the goal can be realized at best in the very distant future, there are several things that can be said now about the way toward it.

The Extension of Consciousness as a Goal

If humanity chooses to work toward the eventual creation of a universal consciousness, to what will it have committed itself now? Obviously we cannot go in one step from the human mind to a universal consciousness. The process must be a gradual one, with many intermediate stages, each of which will possess higher forms of consciousness than ours. Therefore, we can work toward this goal by efforts to develop these higher forms of consciousness. In order to do this, we will have to understand consciousness much better than we do now.

An important step would be a better understanding of its physiochemical aspects. Scientists have not for the most part been very active in this field, perhaps for lack of good research ideas to pursue. One consequence of adopting the goal would be to stimulate such research. As an outgrowth of this, we might expect to be able to initiate some of the qualitative changes in human consciousness discussed above. These might involve chemical and electrical stimulation of the brain, or some form of biological engineering to produce individuals naturally capable of the new forms of consciousness. Both of these would be rational uses of the technological possibilities we have discussed earlier, along lines which are now indicated by our ultimate goal.

Another important approach would be to see whether consciousness can occur in association with anything other than animal or human brains, in particular, whether electromechanical systems can be made that satisfy the criteria we believe vital for consciousness. Although it appears likely that consciousness is a result of the physiochemical structure of the human brain and there is in principle no reason why other physical systems could not be constructed that would be conscious, it is possible that this is wrong and something unexpected is involved here. We cannot be certain about this until we are capable of producing consciousness artificially. I do not know of any systematic research along these lines.

A third avenue that could be explored is the attainment of distinctively different mental states by presently constituted men, perhaps by a more intensive effort to induce and study mystic experiences and the experiences occurring under the influence of various drugs. I do not know to what extent these can be studied successfully by the standard methods of science, but surely much more can be done with them than has been until now. Most scientists' reaction to such experiences has been so colored by emotional factors as to prevent their objective study. The same is, of course, true of those who have had the experiences. If a somewhat more dispassionate attitude existed, it is likely that we would learn much more.

But while I believe that a study of mystical and drug experiences is a valuable step toward the ultimate extension of consciousness, a wholesale commitment of the human race to the mystic life, or to a drugged life, is not consistent with this goal. It is hard to see how we could continue beyond the first step if such a commitment were made, since there is no indication that mystics or drug users are interested in matters beyond their immediate experience. Therefore, even if these experiences represent an improvement over the ordinary human condition, if we wish to play for the higher stakes represented by the creation of the universal consciousness, we will have to avoid committing all of our energies to these experiences. The life of the mystic may be a worth-while one for some people now and an important aspect of our future development, but it involves a freezing of the human mold at too early a stage to be satisfactory as the way for all of us.

Still another line to be pursued in the extension of consciousness is to attempt a merger between distinct minds. It may be that this will first be possible, after we have created machine consciousness, either between several of the conscious machines, or between a machine mind and a human mind, since we could try to design the machine so as to make such a linkup easy, whereas for two human beings it is obviously not easy. Nevertheless, the merger of human minds is also something to be looked into; perhaps it will be an outgrowth of the better scientific understanding of consciousness.

Finally, it would be of great interest to know more about where consciousness occurs in the universe now; whether other animals on earth than man are conscious, and if so where consciousness first arises in living things; at what point in the development of an individual human being he first becomes conscious, and what the attendant changes in behavior are. We should also embark on the long search for conscious beings in other parts of the universe through some form of communication with other stellar systems. With more knowledge of the present range of consciousness in the universe, we will be in a better position to estimate how far we must go to make it universal. Perhaps we can also learn new things about consciousness from other beings that possess it.

Because of the millennial nature of the goal of extending consciousness, we can expect that, if we adopt it, it will exert a small but persistent influence on human activities over a very long period of time. A large part of the human race will not immediately go to work in this area, especially since we have as yet no clear idea of how to proceed. But some philosophical effects, such as a consensus on the importance of consciousness, and perhaps a greater respect for the vehicles of it, that is, one another, would be fairly immediate.

More important than any immediate effects is that this goal would provide an ethical court of last resort for decisions during the entire future of the human race. In listing some of the early steps we would take if we chose to follow this goal, I have shown how the choice would help us decide how to deal with some of the possibilities that technology will open to us. Obviously, some of the issues involved in these decisions are subtle enough to require a detailed analysis. The goal of extending consciousness would, however, like any long-term goal we might choose, simplify the analysis considerably, and in some cases make the answer as to what our decision should be obvious. This holds not only for technological advances that may become possible anyway, but, more importantly, for deciding in what directions we should concentrate our efforts.

The most obvious conclusion for making decisions to be drawn from the goal of extending consciousness is that we should not encourage any developments that would freeze the psychic nature of mankind in its present state. This would be to abdicate our ability to aid directly in the evolution of consciousness. The evolution might occur anyway, either through the tortuously slow processes of biological evolution or through the efforts of another species, but we would have missed our opportunity to play an active role in the process. Thus, the systematic introduction of "dream machines," for example, would not be consistent with the goal of extending consciousness, because a world of dreamers would not progress in any direction, let alone extend consciousness.

The actual extension of consciousness, as opposed to the goal of extending consciousness, would have radical effects on human life. When any of the higher levels of consciousness becomes technically possible, people's reactions to it will vary. Some will want to enter into this new stage, or to have their children do so if they themselves cannot. Others may not desire the change in the most intimate part of their being that would be involved in an alteration of their consciousness. We must respect these individual preferences and regard the extension of consciousness as a potentiality the individual may or may not choose for himself, even though this may lead to a few individuals, through their own choice, being left out of experiences the rest of mankind finds desirable.

I think that we cannot, however, allow people to determine the lives of their children in this respect. If some extension of consciousness becomes possible for everyone, through some form of genetic engineering, there may be valid reasons for not extending the treatment to the whole new generation, such as uncertainty about the long-term effects, but I believe that the step is too important in the life of an individual to let the prejudices of his parents determine this part of his fate.

A question of special poignancy, which Stapledon touches upon, is the relationship between superconscious beings and humans of the type that now exist.[35] It is possible that we would resent our successors, even though we consciously created them. It is also possible that they would dismiss our efforts and concerns as petty and unimportant. But I think not. I would imagine that with a higher form of consciousness would come a much deeper concern for all consciousness, whatever its stage of development. Therefore I believe that the reaction of the superconscious to humanity will be a mixture of wonder at what it aspired to do and sadness at its limitations. The universal consciousness that is our ultimate goal will perhaps feel this way about all the finite consciousnesses that have preceded it. But perhaps in some way that we cannot imagine they will be a part of this final state. This is what Stapledon seems to be saying in *Death into Life*.

If we embark on the path of extending consciousness, we will have to learn to do many new things before we can accomplish much. In fact, it is hard to see anything immediate we could do along these lines, apart from encouraging the kinds of research into consciousness I have described above. It is impossible to say how long it will take to solve some of the scientific problems involved in extending our consciousness, but the very fact that we can formulate some of them now suggests that it may be possible within a few centuries. I would guess that the most rapid progress will be made in the area of machine consciousness and in producing links between man and machine. Machines are much more malleable than humans, and there are less likely to be moral objections to what is done to machines than to changes made in human beings. But I would also not be too surprised if this prediction turns out to be wrong and the next step in consciousness involves purely organic beings.

The time scale of a few centuries and the knowledge of where we are trying to go make it possible for us to adapt our social institutions to the situation when the new form of consciousness becomes a reality. One of the things we could do soon, if we adopted the goal of extending consciousness, would be to begin thinking about what kind of society would go with the new forms of consciousness.

What form a human society would take if its members achieved a heightened consciousness is a fascinating speculation. Suppose people whose minds had been merged had to live together in as close an arrangement as the present family. New social institutions would have to be devised to make this systematically possible. One might guess that these institutions would involve intimate associations between larger numbers of people than anything we have yet seen, but this would depend on the form taken by the extended consciousness. If on the other hand links between men and machines are involved, it could result in weaker ties between human beings. Stapledon gives some interesting descriptions of what a society might be like in which there was a kind of shared consciousness in *Last and First Men*,[36] in the section dealing with the "last" men. While Stapledon's time scale seems to me many orders of magnitude longer than what will be necessary, his vision of the possibilities of human societies and achievements is quite extraordinary.

My case for choosing the extension of consciousness as a long-range goal can be summarized by the positive advantage of the extension of consciousness and the disadvantage of maintaining our present state. Consciousness is the most precious thing man possesses; indeed, it is what makes him man. To extend it would therefore be to enrich ourselves and the universe in the quality most worth having and to act in the most direct way to alleviate the present main source of our discontent.

Whatever man becomes, or becomes capable of, consciousness is likely to remain important to him, and this goal is therefore relatively stable against unforeseen developments. This is particularly important because of the indefinite time scale involved, since the longer we go on, the more likely such developments are to occur. The one thing that might have a really substantial effect would be if we learn that mind is truly independent of matter and not explicable in terms of the laws of physics. Even this would not necessarily force us to alter our goal, but it would certainly make it necessary to reconsider our approach.

The chief arguments against choosing to extend consciousness, at least at the present time, are that we do not yet know how to go about this, or even if it can be done intentionally, and would therefore be committing ourselves to an indefinite, open-ended effort to achieve something we cannot now fully understand. These objections are true of many long-range goals, and they do not persuade me. The goal I propose is essentially to transcend what we are now, in the respect most important to us. This could hardly be easy to accomplish, and we cannot expect to encompass what we shall become in our present imagination. This does not make the goal less desirable or the effort less worth while. We will not *know* what we can achieve until we try.

I hope that humanity will share my feelings about this goal, but, as I have said before, any proposed goal, and the extension of consciousness in particular, is an expression of the feelings of the proposer, not basically a matter of logic. The need for agreement on some goals, on the other hand, and the inauguration of the Prometheus Project in order to reach such agreement is a matter for logical decision.

V. Philosophical Problems in Setting Goals

One of the unfortunate consequences of the lack of systematic effort to set goals for the human race is that there has been no study of the philosophical questions involved. I have in mind such questions as:

What proportion of the time of individuals is to be spent working toward group goals?

Should the goals of the human race be set by a small elite group, or by as many people as wish to take part in the discussion?

What ethical decision is involved if those now alive set a goal that only future generations can fulfill, that is, should the present bind the future to its own purposes?

Questions of the kind outlined above are about goals in general rather than about any specific goal. Nevertheless, such questions must be answered if we are to know what we are doing in setting goals for ourselves.

When I say that we need a philosophy of goal-setting, I am using the word philosophy like the analytic philosophers, in the sense of a logical analysis of a set of concepts or a mode of thought, rather than as a detailed system of beliefs. What is involved is a clarification of the concepts and words being employed, rather than insights into a subject matter that exists independently. I do not believe that there are abstract truths waiting to be discovered about the setting of goals. I do believe that by examining the questions suggested above and others like them, we can learn where there are substantial issues, and what these issues are. Once we know this, the role of analytic philosophy is over, and other considerations, either scientific or moral, are required to go further.

There are three kinds of philosophical questions about goals: those that refer to the process of considering and agreeing to long-range goals; those that refer to the goals themselves; and those that refer to the effects that agreeing on long-range goals would have on society and on individuals within the society.

REACHING AGREEMENT ON GOALS

Since there has never been any search for long-range goals by a substantial fraction of the world, there are matters of principle that are unclear involved in the search itself. In some cases, the answers can be given only after the search begins; a certain amount of faith is involved in starting out, just as it is in many other human activities.

The first question is whether there really are group goals we can agree upon. It might be argued that the differences in heredity and upbringing between various individuals are so great as to make a general consensus very unlikely, particularly in view of the difficulties sometimes encountered in reaching agreement in even small homogeneous groups of people, such as families.

The only conclusive way of determining whether humanity can agree upon its goals is to attempt to do so. No purely logical or psychological arguments can be wholly convincing, because we do not yet understand the basic process by which mass movements occur among people. It is, for example, difficult to determine by the currently known principles of social psychology, why the faith of Islam should have spread as rapidly as it did. Nevertheless, I think that plausible arguments can be given that agreement on long-term goals is not out of the question for a major part of humanity.

One piece of evidence pointing in this direction is the success of a number of historical mass movements in obtaining the acquiescence of a relatively large number of people to general goals.[1] Earlier examples of such movements were religiously inspired, while some of the more recent ones, such as nationalist movements, are more secular. In these cases, however, the actual formulation of the goals is not really a group process, and I therefore regard their success only as an indication that under certain conditions people are open to conviction about the kind of matters involved in setting long-range goals. No mass movement has yet encompassed all of humanity, but the step from 25 percent, the amount involved in, say, Christianity, to nearly 100 percent may not be too difficult, particularly in view of the advance in communications.

On those goals that involve correcting flaws in the human condition, it seems reasonable to suppose that, to the extent that these flaws are recognized as universal, some proposal to correct them could be agreed upon. Indeed, given the agreement that there is a flaw, and a wish to correct it, the problem becomes to some extent one of means, rather than ends.

It may be objected that I have assumed too much in accepting the premise of general agreement on flaws in the human condition, and I have already acknowledged that one's evaluation of these is based largely on feeling rather than fact. There are, however, places, such as the perception of pain, where each man is the best judge of his own feelings, and yet there can be universal agreement on the phenomenon. Therefore, if there really are universal flaws in man's condition, we need not despair of people's recognizing them.

What about agreement on positive goals? There are many things each man finds good in the world. It is even likely there are some things that everyone agrees are good and worth striving to accomplish. But this could not be called agreement on the goals of the human race. What is missing is knowledge of the choice that is being made. One's attitude toward the value of some action is usually influenced by the consequence of holding that attitude, and people might feel differently than they would otherwise about something if they knew it was to be adopted as a common goal. Therefore we cannot be satisfied with taking the intersection of all individual preferences and calling this the goals of humanity. We must instead consciously try to imagine circumstances that we would be satisfied to accept as goals. When examples of these are suggested by individuals, the rest of us can consider how appealing they are. As no such process has been tried before, it is impossible to predict that it will lead to agreement. It is, however, a human trait to be willing to try things whose success is uncertain, providing the possible returns are sufficiently attractive. So if men are convinced of the need for agreement on long-range goals, the uncertainty of reaching such agreement will not deter them.

Who should actually be involved in the search for goals? I have already stated that I believe it should involve a sizable portion of the human race, indeed, as many people as are willing to take part in it. It could, however, be maintained that a more workable system would be to have a small number of intellectually or morally gifted persons entrusted with the job of formulating goals for all of us. This would be an extension of the system followed in the past, where a single religious leader or philosopher chose the goals. It can be argued in favor of this latter view that most of humanity is so concerned with personal matters that it is unwilling or unable to think about anything as abstract as long-range goals. These should therefore be decided by a small group capable of thinking about the question, which could be representative of all segments of humanity.

I believe that this system has such severe defects that it is totally unacceptable. Any small, homogeneous group chosen on the basis of intellectual distinction, worldly success, ability to win elections, or any of the usual methods, is likely to represent a very restricted sample of the thoughts and feelings of humanity as a whole, and any goal or set of goals proposed by such a group would be likely to emphasize the particular interests of the group. If the decision were left to the most brilliant men, the goals would be highly intellectual; if left to a group of theologians, highly theological.

But what we need are goals wide enough to encompass all men that can help us decide between courses of action that will affect all mankind. Furthermore, the chances that the remainder of humanity will willingly accept goals proposed by any special group seems very small, precisely because the goals are likely to reflect the interests of their proposers. Goals obtained in this way would have to be imposed from above on an indifferent population, the very opposite of what I envisage as the way people should react to true goals.

I see no alternative to opening the selection to all who wish to take part in it. Indeed, I think we should encourage as many people as possible to play an active role in both suggesting goals and evaluating those suggested by others. Only through such group participation can the whole enterprise become meaningful to most people, and only if the goals are meaningful will there be real dedication to them once they have been chosen.

It is no contradiction to say that the search for goals must be a group effort even though the formulation of ideas is in all cases the work of an individual mind. Humanity will participate in the search for goals as individuals, but the individuals will not qualify because they are intellectuals, or holy men, or politicians, but only because they are interested human beings.

The methods by which large numbers of people can express their views on human goals is a problem not of philosophy, but of social organization, and therefore will be discussed in the last chapter.

The last question to be considered here is whether twentieth-century man knows enough about himself and the world to warrant setting goals for the distant future. I maintained in Chapter II that the remaining gaps in our knowledge of the natural world were not so great as to disqualify us from such an enterprise. A more serious objection would be the lack of a clear understanding of our own mental lives, the sources of our motivations, and the conditions that would lead to happiness. So long as these questions remain open, it could be argued that any decision on long-range goals was futile, since even if the goal were achieved it would not satisfy us.

It must be granted that the origin of the motivations of individuals or the circumstances under which an individual would be happy are still largely mysterious to us. Even the individual is often mistaken if he is asked to predict whether or not some particular state would make him happy. But these problems are less important if we are trying to make statements about groups of men, because the individual factors tend to average out. While one cannot be sure that one woman will be happier married than not, it seems safe to say that most women will be. Since we are trying to set group goals, the lack of assurance that achievement of the goals will make a given individual happy is not entirely relevant.

It is, however, worth while to consider the most serious case, so let us assume that there are serious gaps in our understanding. Even this circumstance should not destroy our desire to plan for the distant future. In any situation, human beings must plan and act on the basis of the best information they have. This information is never complete, and uncertainty is a constant companion to human thought. But this does not paralyze the will to act in healthy individuals, and it should not for the human race.

In the life of an individual, it is often necessary to plan for the future when choosing a career, or a spouse, or whether to have children. In matters like this our information is also imperfect. We cannot, of course, be sure whether a profession or a person chosen at the age of twenty will appeal to the person we will be at forty or how successful we will be at our chosen work. Nevertheless, we do not hesitate to make such decisions on the basis of the information we have, if only because there is nobody we trust to make them for us.

But although the possible fallibility of our knowledge should not deter us from choosing goals, we should not be completely oblivious to it either. Perhaps a reasonable procedure would be first to choose goals as if what we believe were actually true and then try to imagine how the goal would have to be modified if some element of our knowledge were proven false. This might suggest certain internal safeguards that could be built into the efforts to reach the goal, such as diversity in the social forms encouraged during the intermediate stages. If there are many roads available to reach some goal, a new discovery may not destroy them all, and we would then be grateful that we had set up many different paths.

This procedure is no proof against real surprises or discoveries that violate ideas so deeply held that they are taken for granted in all discussions—for example, a discovery that it is possible to communicate with the dead. It is impossible to make any predictions about the likelihood of such discoveries, and the most reasonable procedure is to disregard the possibility that they will occur when making plans. If some such discovery, which conflicts with one of the goals we have chosen, is made in the future, future generations will have to change the goal in conformity with their new knowledge. I do not think that it will be held against us that we planned on the basis of the best information we had.

SOME QUESTIONS ABOUT LONG-RANGE GOALS

In order to help define what is meant by long-range goals, it is useful to consider some general questions relevant to all such goals.

It is important to consider how the goals of mankind differ from the goals of subgroups of the human race or of individuals. Does taking into account the interests of the whole human race open up any new goals that would be inappropriate for a smaller group, and, conversely, are some of the possible goals of smaller groups inappropriate for the whole race?

It is fairly clear that some goals of subgroups are inappropriate for the whole human race because subgroups which are generally much more homogeneous may therefore have special interests not shared by others. The systematic understanding of the relations between natural phenomena, which is of paramount interest to scientists, may not be of very great interest to most of humanity, particularly insofar as it is separated from its applications. If this is the case, understanding all of nature cannot be a goal of the human race. It can, however, still be a goal of the subgroup that find it interesting, as indeed it has always been. But it will not then have the same ethical priority as the goals of the race.

The goals of some groups may also introduce

distinctions between the value and role of different people that are not acceptable outside the
subgroup. This includes the attitudes of White
Supremacists, Nazis, and believers in a religiously
elect people, such as the Ancient Jews or the
Calvinists. Since such assumptions violate the
principle of the unity of mankind, which was our
starting point, it is highly unlikely that any goals
based on them could be accepted as goals of
humanity, although again, they might remain
goals of the groups accepting the assumptions.

Finally, the goals of subgroups are usually
too restricted in time and scope to be interesting
as long-range goals for the human race. These
groups last for only a short time compared to the
life of the human race, and their goals are generally limited by this consideration. This is particularly true of the personal goals of individuals,
which rarely go beyond the lifetime of the person. I think that it also holds for such groups of
people as nations, insofar as they can be said to
have goals. For example, an inquiry into the
goals of the United States, carried out in the
1950s by a Presidential Commission, produced
no goal extending beyond about twenty years.[2]
Perhaps this is because nations are to some extent set up through accidental circumstances. As
a result, a particular nation's goals may be very
strongly conditioned by the accidental circumstances of its birth, or of some crisis in its history, which is irrelevant for humanity as a
whole.[3]

This need not be the case. The general principles in the Declaration of Independence or the Declaration of the Rights of Man transcend the national groups that invented them. But, for this very reason, they have become part of the general legacy of human ideas and are not really very closely associated with individual nations any longer. This phenomenon is, however, rather rare. The usual situation is that the explicit or implicit goals of a given nation relate very closely to the character of that nation, and are not general enough to qualify as humanity's goals.

Let us now examine briefly the converse question of whether by considering goals for the human race we open up new possibilities beyond the goals of subgroups. We have already seen that the greater time scale available to the human race makes it feasible to consider goals with a longer time span. This is particularly relevant to what I have called final goals where the time scale is the indefinite future. It is hard to see how any subgroup of the human race could entertain such goals.

Another feature of the goals of humanity is that if all of humanity can agree on a goal, it is unlikely that conflicts between men will occur in the implementation of it. The attempt to achieve the goals of most groups involves conflicts with other groups, which may not only make it difficult to reach the goal, but also may change the very sense of it. This has been the case with most of the goals of religious groups throughout history, and it is another reason why I think that essentially unanimous agreement, rather than majority rule, is crucial in the choice of long-range human goals. Otherwise, serious conflicts are likely to ensue between the proponents and opponents. The goals of humanity should be a means for uniting it, not of dividing it further.

Finally, there is the obvious point that the human race exceeds in numbers, range of ability, and available resources, any of its subgroups. Therefore, it can consider for itself goals that would probably be impossible for any smaller group of people. The systematic exploration of space, for example, is feasible only for the combined human race. An interesting question, to which I will return below, is whether there are goals so difficult that even the whole of humanity is unequal to the task.

The second question, which has already been mentioned, whether the present can and should bind the future to its own purposes, has both a practical and an ethical aspect. In a society intellectually committed to freedom of choice by adults, there appears to be something distasteful about making plans that will restrict the free choice of future generations, who have had no say in the decision, and this feeling accounts for much of the distrust of long-range planning, particularly among those who believe that future men will be wiser than we and so better able to plan their lives.

The fact is that we have no option about influencing the lives of future men no matter what we do. The world that future men will be born into will come about as a result of our choices. An inescapable result of the one-way flow of time is that we are all born into a world we never made. Therefore, we cannot help but restrict the choice of future men, if only through the influence on their world of the free choices that we ourselves make.

Of course, we may feel that we should strive to leave as many options as possible open to our descendants. This in itself might be a long-range goal. I think, however, that it is too vague to be valuable. The number of available courses of action is so large that it seems hardly possible to determine how many of them we are eliminating and how many we are opening by some decision.

Since we will inevitably influence the future through our actions, the question is simply how. The procedure usually followed in the past was to act and let the consequences follow, without trying to anticipate what these would be in the long run and without providing any intellectual guide to what aim was being pursued. The proposal of this book is that we instead analyze the kind of future we wish to bring about and then act accordingly, having made clear to ourselves and our descendants what our aims are. In this way, although these descendants will still be born into a world they did not plan, at least their world will to some extent have been planned by somebody, and there will be somebody they can blame if they have any complaints.

There is another side to this question. The modifications of man that may be required to implement the goals we choose may involve biological changes of the kind discussed in Chapter III or psychological conditioning of future generations so that the goals seem desirable to them as well. The latter procedure, similar to that described in Aldous Huxley's *Brave New World*,[4] has seemed abhorrent to many people. Yet to be raised in any society is to be conditioned into certain beliefs and forms of behavior. In most cases the conditioning is done unconsciously, and the beliefs are tacit. I do not think that any new moral principle is established if we do the conditioning consciously, in connection with explicit principles. It is a question of what the principles that are instilled into future generations are to be, and it would seem that the freely chosen goals of the human race are worthy candidates.

Nevertheless, it would probably be wise not to make the conditioning too perfect. Future men should have the ability to question the goals we set for them, if only because they may learn things that we did not know. Perhaps we should simply rely on the continuity of human thought and feeling to ensure that future generations will find the goals we choose worthy of their continued effort.

Short of psychological conditioning, there is no way we can guarantee that the future will remain committed to the goals we have chosen. Such a continued commitment will, however, be more likely if we can make a strong, explicit case for our goals than if we leave them tacit and unexamined. If the goals we choose express something fundamental about human thought and feeling, we will have what assurance is possible that they will remain relevant so long as humanity persists in its present form. If our goals are inaccurate in this sense, then, if we have convinced our descendants of the need for long-range goals, we can rely on them eventually to produce a better set. In the meantime, we will have had the guidance of the principles that seemed best to us to help us in the decisions we must make.

The problem of the continued commitment of future generations to the goals we set is part of the general question of our likelihood of success. Since some of the goals may take millennia or longer to achieve, there is little chance that those who set them will live to see them accomplished, unless and until control over aging is accomplished. It is therefore particularly important that we have some kind of intellectual conviction that the goals we choose and work toward will be accomplished in the fullness of time, otherwise the whole enterprise may be rejected as too much of a gamble. What then are the elements entering into success at achieving long-range goals?

One is that our goals be consistent with the laws governing natural processes, which many of the goals conceived by earlier men were not. We understand the universe and man's place in it much better now, and, given that understanding, the laws of nature do not place very severe restrictions on what we can accomplish.[5] Through our scientific knowledge and technological ability, we can be fairly confident that there will be no technical barriers to the accomplishment of our goals.

Another consideration is the stability of human societies and their institutions over long periods of time. If we adopt goals that will take millennia to accomplish and set up institutions to help accomplish them, we must ask whether those institutions will persist over the necessary time periods. There has not been much experience with such matters in human history. The longest periods over which social institutions have remained roughly constant have been a few centuries, in the case of some political and religious institutions.[6] We do not know whether there is some general historical law that would explain why fundamental changes in social institutions occur over periods longer than a few centuries, and in the absence of such knowledge, we cannot tell whether any given methods we choose now will continue to be applicable. Nevertheless, even though the institutions may change, if men remain committed to the goal, it may still come about. After all, the scientific institutions of today are very different from the Royal Society in Newton's time, yet they pursue the same goal.

Whether men will remain committed to our goals is, of course, also questionable. Human attitudes change over long periods of time, for reasons that are difficult to understand or foresee. Such a change in feeling might destroy the interest in a particular long-range goal or perhaps in all long-range goals, not because of anything having to do with the goals themselves, but because of other unrelated developments in human life. For instance, the decline in religious feeling and of interest in religious goals that has marked the world in the past few centuries has to a large extent been spurred by the rise of science, which seems to have been a process independent of religion. One can imagine similar developments taking place in the future, which would change our attitudes about what is important.

I believe it is neither feasible nor desirable to control human life so much that such a change in attitude could not occur. This is not, however, to say that nothing can be done to decrease its probability. One reason why long-range goals are needed is to help make decisions about how to proceed with technological innovations. These decisions will determine some of the future course of human life. If they are to be made consistent with our long-range goals, we can take into account how their consequences could affect future attitudes toward these goals, and modify the decisions accordingly if necessary.

For example, if we adopted any goals other than increasing individual pleasure to the highest possible degree, we would probably wish to exercise great care in the use of "dream machines," which, if developed and used by many people, might divert attention from the goals we were trying to accomplish. Therefore, while I see no a priori moral ground for eliminating dream machines, if their development would conflict with other aims we now consider more important, I think we should feel free to inhibit it, as we should any developments in human life we can foresee that might lead to abandonment of long-range goals that we have chosen. It is those developments whose effects we cannot foresee that we cannot forestall, without paying what is I think the exorbitant price of an overcontrolled society. Others may differ with these views, which is why I state them here explicitly.

It is also possible that the rapid change in morals, esthetics, etc., that has characterized our period will not persist in the future, especially after we have adopted long-range goals to give a direction to human life. There are, as we have seen, probably not many surprises left for us to discover concerning the natural world, and scientific discoveries are one of the things that color the esthetic and moral judgments of an age when they are eventually assimilated into the public consciousness. On the other hand, the pace of technological change is, if anything, increasing, and, as we have also seen, this is likely to lead to changing moral attitudes as well. It is hard to tell which of these factors will dominate, and whether there will be increased or decreased stability in what people consider important and valuable in the future.

Therefore, if we are to allow future men the same free choice I am recommending for ourselves, we cannot be sure that they will continue to favor our goals and there can be no guarantee that the goals we choose will be pursued to a successful conclusion. But this is a part of what it means to be human, both for individuals and for groups. In no human enterprise is success assured, so we can hardly expect it here, in the most ambitious of our efforts. What we must do is to choose our goals as well as we can and devote our best efforts to their accomplishment. This will at least satisfy our own motivations and perhaps provide a good enough example for our descendants that they will not idly discontinue our work. If it should work out otherwise, at least we can be comforted by the thought that we have followed the best strategy open to finite men, with unlimited dreams.

THE GOAL-DIRECTED SOCIETY

If the adoption of long-range goals is a vital step for the human race to take, it follows that human life and human institutions would be seriously affected by the step. It is therefore important to examine some of the problems that may arise in a society that has adopted long-range goals. Some problems will depend on the specific goals chosen. Others, however, would occur whatever the goals, and it is these that I want to discuss here.

First of all, we would have to decide whether society should require its members to devote a certain fraction of their efforts to the group goals, whether or not they would spontaneously do so.

The demands that society can legitimately make upon its members has been a problem for political thinkers at least since Plato. Almost all organized societies make some such demands, whether in the form of required labor, as in China, or service in the armed forces, or through the payment of taxes. If we use the last as a measure, then in the industrialized countries, some 10 to 20 percent of the productive labor is diverted to the purposes of the central government,[7] which might be taken as an indication of the fraction of one's effort devoted to the purposes of society in these countries. Much of this effort is devoted to such activities as national defense, road building, etc., which have always been considered the responsibility of government. Indeed, for some social theorists these are the purposes of governments. But in many societies a part of the government's revenue has been used for artistic, scientific, religious, or other cultural purposes as well. Sometimes this has been done without the consent of the people, in other cases with their eager assistance. I would take this as establishing the moral principle that societies can make some demands on the efforts of their members for ends that go beyond the minimal purposes for which governments are set up.

Therefore someone who accepts the legitimacy of these additional activities of governments should agree that when the human race adopts group goals, it can call upon individuals to devote some of their work to achieving these goals. How great an individual effort could be required and the forms this could take are other matters. The imposition of taxes is a relatively painless way of obtaining such effort, as long as the tax rate is not extreme. For some group goals, however, a specific kind of individual work might be necessary, which could not be replaced by a tax. For example, if we choose the goal of systematically eliminating human suffering, then insofar as this suffering is caused by the actions of one person toward another, it would become necessary to require certain efforts of each individual, such as going out of his way to be kind to the unfortunate.

But there must be some limit to how many of an individual's actions can be prescribed by group goals. Individuals should not set aside their own goals and devote themselves single-mindedly to the group goals. As we are now constituted, each man is most accurately thought of as a separate entity whose actions and desires, although they have been influenced by society, are individual and distinctive. The efforts in some societies to submerge the will of the individual in the "general will" of the group have by and large been ineffective, if only because the consciousness of each man is individual and not shared. Unless we choose to change this particular aspect of man, we must accept the fact that individuals will maintain their personal lives and goals, which will be largely independent of the group goals. This is something to be not deplored, but recognized. Nothing I have said in this book should be taken to imply that I regard the goals of the human race as higher or more important than the motivations of individual men. Indeed,

I believe that the feelings of individuals are the source of all ethical principles, and I regard the goals of the human race as another aspect of the same feelings that are the source of individual motivations. The group goals refer to a consensus of those aspirations we have in common, while our personal goals come from those feelings that distinguish each one of us. These personal goals are an alternative source of motivation for individual action, and any individual will be at least as interested in accomplishing them as in contributing to the goals of the human race. Therefore, some allocation of priorities is required between personal and group goals for determining an individual's activities.

Such priorities cannot be decided on in advance for all goals. The different group goals that might be adopted would have a wide variety of time scales associated with them, which would by itself influence the fraction of each man's effort that their accomplishment would require. A goal that would take a million years to accomplish is likely to make much smaller demands on each of us next year than a goal we want to achieve in fifty years. Furthermore, some goals do not require the direct efforts of many people, and would therefore not directly influence the activities of most people during this period. The amount of commitment required of most individuals would be no more than not opposing the efforts of those working toward them, together with perhaps some indirect contribution in the form of a tax. Other goals would need specific activities from each individual, which could conflict with his own goals, and in those cases, an order of priorities would have to be decided upon.

Of course, humanity may be unwilling to accept goals that require too great an effort by each of us to fulfill. Hence the discussions of specific goals should keep this problem in mind.

Possible conflicts may also arise between the goals of humanity and the activities and goals of intermediate groups—either political groups such as nations or interest groups such as theoretical physicists. Since the aims of these groups will sometimes be inconsistent with the goals of humanity, some principle must be established for dealing with these conflicts too.

I think that we would be justified in establishing a priority for the goals of the race over the goals of smaller groups whenever these conflict. One reason for agreeing upon long-range goals is to use them in making decisions on matters of vital concern to humanity, which will often conflict with the wishes of different small groups. Therefore, if the long-range goals of humanity are to help in making the decisions, we must agree that they have a higher moral status than the principles followed by the subgroups of humanity.

This attitude is consistent with the view that the goals of humanity should not always be taken as morally higher than the personal goals of individuals. Whereas individuals are the units of mind and will and therefore have a claim to special treatment on those grounds, most groups of men come about arbitrarily and have no distinctive character that would justify giving their aims any special role. If we accept the principle that all men are of equal value, the principles that all men can agree to should be given a higher moral status than those principles that are restricted to smaller groups.

This could lead to restrictions on the characteristic activities of some groups. Scientists might not be permitted to carry some forms of research to the point where their consequences could conflict with some long-range goals—say in connection with the construction of intelligent machines. Those activities of nations that might endanger the survival of the human race, which is a prerequisite for most long-term goals, would also be restricted.

How such restrictions could be accomplished is part of a more general question. Experience with other efforts to follow abstract principles in guiding human societies, such as Christianity in medieval Europe or Marxism in contemporary Europe, has indicated that the actual content of the principles is determined to a large extent by the methods through which they are applied.[8] The institutions that are supposed to interpret the principles in particular cases and apply them to the problem at hand are of particular importance. Let us therefore consider what methods and institutions might exist for working toward long-term goals in a society that had agreed upon some such goals.

One question that occurs immediately is whether there should be some new organization specifically devoted to carrying out these goals. As an alternative, we can imagine that some government, perhaps a world government if one is set up, could do this in addition to its other functions. Another alternative would be that existing organizations whose general activities are in the area of the specific goal that has been chosen could coordinate the work toward its accomplishment. Although each of these approaches has its advantages and disadvantages, I think that a specific organization for working to accomplish the long-range goals provides the best solution.

Several functions will have to be performed by whatever organization is responsible for working toward the goals. One is the determination of a plan for getting there. Some of this will have been done in the process of choosing the goal, since the goal is to a certain extent inseparable from the method of reaching it. But a really detailed plan, especially for those goals with a long time scale, must await agreement upon the goal. The plan will also require modifications as it unfolds, since it is extremely unlikely that all eventualities that may occur over several hundred years or longer can be predicted in advance. Therefore, another function of the organization would be to monitor the progress and make whatever changes in the plan might be necessary as a result of new developments. A third function might be to help carry out the job of convincing succeeding generations of the desirability of the goal, through some kind of educational campaign.

Finally, there must be some mechanism for dealing with the inevitable conflicts between the goals of humanity and the activities of smaller groups and of individuals. I do not think that the decisions on the resolution of these conflicts should necessarily be given to the organization working on the goal. Nevertheless, this is clearly one of the questions that it would have to be concerned about.

Let us consider the alternative kinds of organization in the light of these functions they will have to perform. Since the effort will take much longer than one lifetime, the group in charge of it should be highly dedicated to this task, because only such dedicated people are likely to work hard to accomplish it. For the same reason, the organization will have to last for a very long time.

These two points seem to argue strongly in favor of an autonomous organization, as opposed to any government. Organizations with other functions to perform are unlikely to have the single-mindedness necessary to work toward a long-term goal. The world government in particular is likely to have so many other problems in its early stages that it would not be able to concentrate much on planning for long-range goals. The experience of the specialized agencies of the UN, such as UNESCO, indicates that it is difficult for such agencies to act independently of the political differences within the parent organization, even though the function of the agency may have little to do with politics.

Governments that are elected periodically also tend to avoid planning for much longer than their expected term of office, and, even if they do, their successors may reject their plans simply to demonstrate that a change has taken place.

But because of the major effect on human lives that work toward these goals may have, there will have to be some liaison between the government and the organization directing this work. It is hard to escape the conclusion that the government would play the main role in fitting the activities of subgroups to the requirements of the long-range goals. In fact, some of the execution of whatever decisions are taken by the goal-directing organization would presumably fall on a branch of the government, unless we create a separate but parallel structure for the execution of such decisions, which hardly seems practical. But the exact nature of the link between the government and the new organization requires more study than can be given here.

The third possibility is that some organizations that exist for other purposes could take over the direction of the goals. For instance, if a goal were along the lines suggested by some religion, we might consider letting the religious body direct it. I do not think this approach would be wise either. It would be difficult for the organization to separate its other activities from work toward the goal, and, as a result, the goal might take on some aspects that were not in the minds of those who agreed to it originally. Secondly, if more than one long-range goal were adopted, this would mean that several organizations would be involved in carrying them through, which could lead to difficulties in deciding about relative priorities among the different goals. Finally, it seems to me less likely that previously existing organizations would draw the talented people necessary to make the effort a success than would a new organization wholly devoted to the task.

Therefore, a new organization specifically devoted to the long-range goals is probably the most effective way of working toward these goals. I do not mean to imply by this that the work would be restricted to the members of this organization, but simply that the members would be people whose life's work would be furthering long-range goals. For the rest of the human race, contribution to the work would be only a part of their lives, depending on their own interest and the amount of individual commitment required by the particular goals.

What I am describing here is obviously similar in many ways to a universal religious organization with a priesthood and lay supporters. This is not surprising. Religious bodies, particularly the Christian and Buddhist, were invented to deal with problems similar to those we are considering here—long-term efforts toward relatively abstract goals. Therefore, it is reasonable that some of the structures they have devised for their purposes could also serve in a society devoted to long-range goals.

The place where it may be most helpful to pursue this similarity is in the consideration of possible pitfalls in the operation of the goal-directing organization. Historical experience indicates that organizations that exercise a great deal of power over a long period of time may lose their original purpose and become essentially vehicles for the will to power of the men running them. Therefore, while the goal-directing organization will watch over the progress being made toward the goals, there will also have to be a watch over the organization itself, by some part of the remainder of society, in order to curb such tendencies.

As I indicated at the beginning of this chapter, I have dealt with only a few of the questions that might be considered under the heading of the philosophy of goals. Other examples have probably occurred to the reader, and will certainly come up once many people begin to think seriously about long-term group goals. The answers that have been suggested to the questions raised here are only tentative and are meant at most to suggest that there should be no insuperable problems in working out a detailed analysis of the concepts involved in setting long-range goals for the human race.

The result of such analysis would be an understanding of the real ethical and scientific problems involved, after which the problems could be attacked in the way others of their kind are. Two such problems, which have come up in the analysis above, are whether future generations should be allowed to retain the option of renouncing the goals we have set, and what the relative priorities between group goals and personal goals should be. While I have suggested my own opinion as to the answer to these questions, I think that, as with the choice of goals, they can be properly answered only by the human race as a group.

What I am envisaging here is a division of labor, in which the preliminary analysis that poses the basic ethical questions is carried out by those trained for such analysis, that is, philosophers and social scientists. After this is done, the moral decision must be taken by a much wider group, ideally the whole human race. This procedure may seem wasteful to believers in objective ethics, who might think that some of those capable of determining what the moral problems are could also determine what the objective answers to them are. Since I believe that ethical statements merely record subjective preferences, I cannot accept this view, and I am convinced that the moral court of last resort is the consensus of the human race. This holds for both the determination of our goals and for the moral aspects of the procedures we should follow in attaining them. It is therefore now necessary to consider some methods through which we can reach such a consensus.

VI. The Prometheus Project

In the past, major systems of ethical belief were usually formulated by a gifted individual—Buddha, Confucius, Jesus, Muhammad. To be sure, these men were influenced by the background of thought within their culture, but they put their own stamp on the resultant system so strongly that it has always been associated with them. The later diffusion of the system and its eventual adoption by large numbers of people is a more complex phenomenon, in some cases carried out directly by the inventor, in others by his disciples. And it is possible that there were other ethical systems as worthy as those that have survived, which did not spread and therefore were forgotten.

I do not think we should wait for another man gifted at ethics to be born to formulate our goals for us. I doubt that the ideas of any one man, no matter how gifted, can be adequate for the purpose of deciding what the future directions of development of the human race shall be. What we need instead is some method by which a large part of humanity can cooperate in formulating these goals and convincing all men of their desirability, and to this end I am proposing the Prometheus Project, a cooperative effort by humanity to choose its long-term goals.

This effort is not likely to occur spontaneously. An organization is needed to set the process in motion, publicize it, coordinate the ideas of different groups, and deal with the innumerable items of detail that come up in any mass enterprise. I doubt that any existing organization could be adapted to this purpose. It is too likely that they would dilute the search for goals with their own specific ends. I believe that an entirely new group not committed in advance by an existing structure to a particular mode of operation must be created to organize this search.

If we examine what the Prometheus Project should do, and how it might accomplish it, we will be better able to consider what kind of organization we will need and how to set it up. I need not stress that all the suggestions given here are highly tentative and subject to modification.

How to Search for Goals

The first step is to convince a sizable number of people that the search for goals is both necessary and possible, and it is with this purpose in mind that this book has been written. However, no book is likely to influence more than a very small segment of the human race in any reasonable time. Furthermore, books usually reach only an intellectually sophisticated group of people, and I believe that the search for goals should not be restricted to them. Therefore, something must be done to involve those who would not ordinarily think about abstract questions.

The obvious approach is through the mass media, which influence large fractions of the population. By the use of television in the industrialized countries and radio and newspapers in less developed countries, it is possible to communicate with a majority of the world's people, provided that the various governments that control mass media in many places cooperate.

The message conveyed to the world by these methods must be simple, without the abstract argument of a book like this. Basically, it should be that we need long-range goals, and that these goals must be the product of the thought of people everywhere. I have enough belief in human intelligence to think that this message can be understood by almost everyone. And I have enough belief in human responsibility to think that a sizable portion of those hearing it would be willing to start thinking about it. There has never been a call to cooperative action of all men before, to my knowledge. Other mass movements have been against something as well as for something. The Prometheus Project, if it is to succeed at all, must find a common factor in all human aspiration, and it is conceivable that this very requirement may help to convince people of the value of the enterprise.

Thus, the first job for the organization running the Prometheus Project should be a worldwide publicity campaign. This will require both money and influence with the institutions controlling the means of communication, so it will be important to bring political leaders into the organization, although not necessarily in their official capacities. It will not be easy to do this without committing the organization to some particular political views, but I think it essential that we do exactly that, and more thought must be given to how.

The second step in the Prometheus Project is the creation of definite opportunities for people to discuss their ideas about goals with one another, in order to get some indication about the existence of a consensus. I believe it is very important that the individual discussion groups be heterogeneous; homogeneous groups are too likely to limit themselves to the consideration of goals that are of interest only to their group. I do not conceive of the Prometheus Project as looking for compromises between different interest blocks, but rather for those areas of agreement common to all of us.

The discussions could deal with a variety of matters that provide a background for the consideration of goals, such as the human condition. It is vital that we know what men consider good and worth preserving or improving in their lives, and what they think should be eliminated or modified. An agreement on even some aspects of this would go far toward indicating what some of our long-range goals could be. The discussions would also help to answer the question of how homogeneous mankind really is, since an agreement on what is good and bad about our common lot would be a clear indication of our basic similarities.

The first-stage discussion groups should be small and informal, since most people are likely to be put off by large formal gatherings with prepared speeches. The role of the central organization should be to provide contacts between people interested in the Project, to try to ensure that the groups were sufficiently diverse, and to furnish the discussants with what information about goals is available, perhaps summaries of some of the goals proposed in the past. It might be especially valuable for men of one culture to know about such goals from other cultures. As the process goes on, I am sure that the fertility of the human imagination will produce new goals in great numbers for consideration.

The central organization should also encourage the participants in the first discussion groups to report on their ideas so that they may be transmitted to other groups. This will both give the participants the sense that they are part of a large-scale group effort and prevent isolated groups from spending large amounts of time on ideas that do not have a wide appeal. The central organization might analyze the ideas as they come in, for example, to see which ideas turn up independently in many places. It should not, however, act as censor and decide that some ideas are not worth discussing unless the groups themselves provide evidence of this. To emphasize that the central organization is to be the coordinator of the discussions, not their determiner,

I will refer to it as the Prometheus Coordinating Agency or PCA.

The outcome of this stage of the Prometheus Project should be a reasonably large number of ideas for goals that a sizable number of the discussion groups see merit in. But the question of where to set the "passing grade" had best be left until the process is under way.

This preliminary set of suggestions should then be circulated generally to as much of humanity as possible in the hope that it will stimulate interest in the Project among people who find it too hypothetical without any definite goals to consider and induce people to suggest still other goals, which will then be subjected to the same process. It is very important to keep the channels of communication open to those not yet involved in the Project, since we eventually wish to involve everybody whose interest can be aroused.

To carry out the discussion stage, the PCA will need a sizable staff who can work on the organizational details of setting up and promoting the activities of many small groups in different places. This staff should not be composed of people who have their own strong ideas about goals to foster, and it should contain people from as many countries and cultures as possible. It would probably be unwise to locate all members of the PCA in one place, at least in the beginning. But this should not lead to any real problems in the presence of reliable communications systems between different parts of the world. The problem of obtaining a staff will be considered later.

The third step of the Prometheus Project would be a more thoroughgoing consideration of the goals that have been disseminated. The proponents of each goal would produce detailed statements of how they envisage the goal, why they consider it worth pursuing, and some idea of how to go about reaching it.

When these statements are available, it would be helpful to have a general philosophy of goal-setting to help analyze them. The construction of such a philosophy could best be done at this stage, since answers to some of the questions will depend on the particular goals being considered. It is also at this stage, with many more possible goals available, that a further attempt to give a general categorization of goals could be made, since it is always easier to classify things when there is a large sample.

These are two of the places in the Prometheus Project where intellectually gifted people would play an irreplaceable role. Another would be for them to subject the detailed statements of the newly proposed goals to the kind of critical analysis I have attempted here with the goals of the past. Some of this could be done within the PCA, but it should also be part of the general discussion. Presumably, a fair number of the proposed goals would get through the screening process and become candidates for general acceptance.

To explore the possibility of such acceptance, I think it will be necessary to have widespread discussions of the goals, which most of the world could be spectators of, if not participants in. People who strongly favored a particular goal would attempt to convince doubters or opponents, who would have the same opportunity to present their counterarguments, although not necessarily at the same time. The most obvious form for the discussions to take would be worldwide radio and television broadcasts, perhaps transmitted by satellites to individual receivers, a development that will soon be technically possible, with some backup system to reach those who do not have radio or television.

The PCA would have to have some method of getting feedback from the audience to make sure that the discussions were conveying a real sense of what was being proposed to the man in the street. A good part of the reaction from the audience should be spontaneous by this time. If a sizable number of people do not register their opinions on some goal without being prodded, it will probably mean that insufficient interest has been stimulated either in the particular goal or in goals in general, and that will be a strong indication that the goal should not be chosen or that the method of presenting goals has been inadequate.

We can assume that eventually there will be a good deal of interest shown in one or more of the suggested goals. At this point, the PCA should carry out some kind of polling operation to find out the extent of their appeal. Social scientists have developed techniques for depth interviewing,[1] which could be used to obtain information about what people really think of the goals beyond a yes or no response.

The degree of understanding of and commitment to the goals must be determined before a vote is taken on them. It is often lamented that on most public questions, the electorate, which is the source of ultimate responsibility for whatever action is taken, does not have a very deep understanding of what is involved. This understanding must be a matter of central concern to the Prometheus Coordinating Agency. When the ultimate stakes are so high, the decision must be made with as much knowledge as we can bring to bear on it.

I have already remarked that some men are skeptical about the possibility of any large fraction of the world's population attaining such understanding on the grounds that most people have neither the will nor the ability to consider abstract questions such as long-term goals. Intelligence is indeed unevenly distributed among men. However, the majority of mankind has never been asked to think about abstract issues on its own initiative. Indeed it has usually been told not to concern itself with such issues, or to accept the wisdom of others—injunctions not apt to develop whatever abilities for abstract thought most men possess. The Prometheus Project informs the average man that he must think about the goals of mankind, and that the ultimate decision is his to make. This could conceivably bring forth resources of mental ability unsuspected by the skeptics. At least one should retain an open mind about it until it is tried. If the members of the PCA are sincerely dedicated to the proposition that the understanding of goals is possible and essential, I believe that the methods to promote it will be developed.

It is to be hoped and expected that while the education program is going on, there will be a parallel process of spontaneous thought and discussion of goals among the increasing fraction of the world that is aware of them. The PCA can guide the search and provide the flame to set the fire going, but it must eventually become self-supporting.

At this stage we will have reached a crucial point in the course of the Prometheus Project, when it will become reasonable to determine whether there is a consensus on any of the goals. This will, of course, be the test of whether the whole procedure up until this point has been successful, and I would guess that the staff of the PCA will face it with a good deal of trepidation. In fact, there may be some danger that they will keep postponing the day of reckoning, arguing that conditions are not yet ripe for the consensus. There is some justification in leaving the time of testing up to PCA, but it would be unfortunate if it were delayed indefinitely, and steps should be taken to avoid this. It might be worth while to set a target date well in advance, and allow the date to be postponed only by an overriding agreement within the PCA.

An important issue for the PCA to decide is

the type of consensus it will consider effective. Given the way things are, it is very unlikely that literal unanimity could be closely approximated. There are sure to be some people who care nothing about group goals, and others who, despite the best communication system imaginable, will not have heard about the project, not to mention the people who insist on disagreeing with the majority on general principles. These groups cannot be disregarded, especially if they are a substantial part of the population, but I think it is more important to know the ratio between those in favor and those actively opposed to some goal.

It is also important to know the characteristics of these people as a group. It would clearly be a different situation if, for example, a random 10 percent of the population were against the goal of total individualism than if the 10 percent that professes Buddhism were. If a relatively homogeneous minority rejects some goal, the rejection is apt to be connected with whatever makes them homogeneous, such as a common religion. In this circumstance, it may not prove hopeless to convince the minority to change their view, at least for some goals, by getting them to examine the things upon which they agree that may have led them to reject the goal. It might, of course, be aspects of a common upbringing that produce the rejection, and these are unlikely to be affected by this procedure.

On the other hand, rejection of a goal by a heterogeneous minority probably means that there is a fundamental division on this particular goal. In this case, I would doubt that the minority could be swayed. If, however, the minority is not very large, the majority would probably make the attempt anyway. I fervently hope that the effort would be limited to discussion and no coercion would be used. It is, I think, incumbent on the PCA to ensure that what is reached is a consensus, not a triumph of superior force.

It is impossible to predict the outcome of the first effort to see whether there is a consensus on any of the goals. I would think that an agreement by, say, 80 percent of those with an opinion would be a very encouraging response, provided that a significant part of the world, perhaps 50 percent, were in this group. For the sake of further discussion, I will assume that a test vote of the Prometheus Project produces such agreement on a small number (perhaps only one) of the goals that have been considered. The other case, in which there is no substantial agreement on any of the goals, is treated later.

When there is substantial agreement on a few goals, several questions arise about how to proceed. One of these concerns the degree of opposition to a particular choice. Some people may vote against one goal because they prefer others but are not actively opposed to the goal in question. They might be persuaded to cooperate with the large majority favoring the goal, particularly if they would not have to devote a great deal of their effort to working for it. But there may also be a group of people who believe that a particular goal is wrong, who would not be willing to support it under any circumstances. If this is the case for all the goals that have been considered, we will have to decide whether to search for other goals or to proceed with those that have an approximate consensus.

This is a difficult moral problem, and I have no simple answer to propose. I think what would actually happen would depend on the strength of commitment of the two sides of the issue. One useful device might be to have a period of several years in which no action was taken toward implementing such a goal in order to let both the majority and the minority think about their views. At the end of this period, there would be another vote, to see if there had been any change in the percentages of supporters and opponents, and whether those who had taken no position previously had now decided one way or another. It might be wise to do this even if there were almost unanimous agreement at the beginning, since shifts of public opinion over a few years have been known to occur.

During the "cooling off period" there should be further discussion and analysis of the goals. Again, it is important that the majority not coerce the minority, and one way to try to prevent this would be to guarantee equal access to the mass communication media to both sides. The PCA itself must be scrupulously neutral about the merits of any goal, and the staff should therefore not play a very active role in the discussions, although this may be a very hard thing to avoid.

When the interim period is over and a second vote is taken, the most significant thing to note will be whether the percentage of the population with a definite opinion on the goals has approached 100 percent. If it has, and a strong majority in favor of a few of the goals remains, it will be time to face the question of whether to proceed in spite of the dissenters. Based on the way people have behaved in similar situations in the past, I would guess that there would be an overwhelming pressure by the majority to declare one or more of the goals preferred by a large fraction of the population the goals of the human race. Therefore there must be a binding decision in advance of the vote as to how large a majority will be required for this. The PCA could take the lead in suggesting the requirements, which would perhaps involve setting not only the fraction of the population required, but also the distribution of the majority within the population. This is obviously a question that needs a good deal of study by experts. While it would be better if there were real unanimity, it is only realistic to recognize that this very well may not occur, and if we do not accept a close approach to a consensus we may remain without goals, which, I am convinced, will soon be an intolerable situation.

Perhaps dissidents should be exempted from working toward goals that have been chosen against their wishes, if, in return, they agree not to work against the goals. Since the goals are long-range ones, it is not so important if a fraction of the first generation does not work toward them.

Furthermore, if several goals are chosen, almost everyone may be in favor of at least one, and willing to work for it. Indeed, if there are several such goals chosen, there is a fair chance that any given person will be in the minority on one of them. In that case the opportunity to work for goals you favor while not hindering the work of others toward goals you oppose seems a logical compromise.

This problem is really part of the general question of relative priorities between group goals and personal desires. Since this is one of the questions I think should be decided by the human race together, it would be natural to consider it in the discussions at this stage, when the goals have become precise. In other words, the discussion of the goals should now include a consideration of the demands that the procedures for implementing them might make on the lives of individuals. It would be good if some consensus could be reached about how much would be asked of anyone in order to reach the goals, since this could affect whether a particular goal is acceptable at all. But it might also be that only the time scale for achieving the goal would be affected by such restrictions.[2]

If the fraction required for acceptance of a goal is set above one-half and we assume that nobody votes for two goals that are inconsistent, then the goals that are chosen will be consistent with one another, and the attainment of one will not logically preclude the attainment of another. If, however, more than one goal is chosen, there is still likely to be a problem about establishing an order among them. Part of the problem here is the technical one of understanding how work toward one goal could influence work toward another. This will require study by experts, which the PCA should arrange. But there is also an ethical problem, which again should be decided by all men. The decision about whether some goals are more important than others, which is an integral part of the process of choosing goals, must be made because two goals may suggest two different lines of action in a specific case. Suppose we choose total individualism and the extension of consciousness as goals, and successful "dream machines" become possible. The two goals suggest opposite conclusions about whether to allow the development and use of these machines. Therefore, to make this decision, we must know which of the goals we consider more important.

The choice cannot be made on the basis of the fraction of the vote in favor of each goal in the original vote, since this may not represent people's real preference.[3] Instead, the question of order should itself be the subject of wide discussions after a set of goals has been chosen. In these discussions, it would be crucial to keep in mind that all of the goals being discussed have been certified as good, and to avoid becoming divided into factions at the doorstep of our greatest progress toward unity.

The discussions should therefore be informal to keep from freezing people's attitudes by making them publicly advocate their views, and I would expect that a much shorter period would be necessary between the beginning of discussion and the time for a vote than in the earlier stages. The main role of the PCA in this part of the Project would again be publicizing the goals and the vote on them that was to follow and making every effort to ensure that people really understood the goals. This will become more and more crucial as the time for final decision arrives.

When the vote takes place, we might wish to limit the total number of goals finally chosen to a fixed number, decided upon in advance. If the number is large, the dedication to any one of them will probably be reduced appreciably. Also, the more competing goals, the more likely conflicts are to arise in the effort to implement them all. A restriction of the final choice to, say, two or three goals would seem to be a logical step.

All of these preliminaries will set the stage for the ultimate decision. By the time of the vote, everyone should be familiar with all of the goals whose order of merit they are to decide upon. Because of the significance of the step, the final vote should be invested with dignity and ceremony, to help make people conscious of what they are doing, and why. The vote should decide which goal people think is most worth while, which next most worth while, etc. A voting system will have to be devised to do this, and some study of this point by the PCA will be necessary before the vote is held. The result of the vote, and the culmination of the Prometheus Project, would be the naming of the ends the human race has chosen as its long-range goals. I would hope that the outcome would not come as any real surprise to the world, in the sense that people would have a strong feeling for which goals were going to be preferred from the discussions.

The PCA would at this point formally announce to the world what had been chosen to be our long-term goals, and its primary work would be over. If the Prometheus Project is to be successful, however, it must not only produce a list of accepted goals, but also help motivate people to work for these goals. I suggested earlier that this work might best be directed by a new organization specifically designed for this task, but one final job the PCA might do would be to remain in a caretaker capacity until the new organization is formed. I do not think the PCA itself should evolve into the new organization, although there might be some continuity in the staff; the functions to be performed are too different for there to be any real structural relation between the two. But again, this is a matter that can be left for the future to consider.

Suppose no consensus is found on any of the goals suggested in the early discussions. This would suggest that none of the goals proposed was universal enough to appeal to most of humanity, but it would not be conclusive proof that no such goals could be found. Two further steps might be taken: the earlier discussions could be continued in the hope that they would produce new goals with wider appeal; and the results of the vote could be studied to see whether some combination or reformulation of the suggested goals might win more support. For example, if some well-defined groups rejected all reconstructive goals, it might be useful to discuss their reasons with representatives of the groups. In short, a lack of success in the first attempt should be followed by an analysis of where the disagreements lie and an effort to formulate new goals. While success cannot be guaranteed by this or any other procedure, this self-correcting method has proved successful in the case of natural science, and we may expect that if a solution exists to the problem of finding long-range goals, we will come to it in this way.

We must also consider the time scale over which the Prometheus Project might be carried out. I hope I have made clear that I do not think we have unlimited time. Technological advances, and the decisions that they will require, are coming rapidly, and if the goals we choose are to play the role they should in making these decisions, we will have to choose them soon.

The organization of world opinion has never been tried before, but some of the elements involved are not new, and we can estimate the time required for them. The earliest phase of the Prometheus Project, publicity, could perhaps be done in one or two years, judging by the speed with which ordinary information is transmitted and assuming that governments and other groups that control the communications media will cooperate. Because such cooperation is essential, it should be one of the first orders of business for the PCA. Some governments may be persuaded to cooperate only after the Project is in operation, and they see what is happening.

The length of the second, or discussion, phase of the Project is harder to estimate, because here we are seeking new ideas. If we allotted up to ten years, I would expect that a fair number of goals would be proposed. If this does not happen, the procedure is wrong, and something else should be tried.

The third phase of more formal discussion, analysis, and education should take an equal length of time, or possibly longer. The hardest time scale to estimate is the spread of understanding to the whole world; this will involve a feedback arrangement of continual opinion sampling and adjustment of the methods used—processes with which we have had little experience. Some five to ten years for this phase alone might not be far out of line.

This will bring us to the time of the first test of sentiment. Since the vote will have to be carefully analyzed, a period of a year or two should be allotted to the vote and subsequent analysis. The second discussion or "cooling off" period might last two or three more years, or perhaps longer if it seems desirable. In this period decisions would be made about the circumstances of the final vote, exemptions for dissidents, and other matters for group decision.

The final step—the deciding vote, its analysis, and the announcement of the result—would take a relatively short time, probably no more than a few months. So if we add together all of the times we come to a figure of between twenty-five and fifty years for the length of the Prometheus Project. This means that the people involved in the PCA might expect to see results from their efforts within their working lives, which should make these efforts more willing. The time is also comparable to what I would guess will bring some of the more spectacular technological advances, such as artificial intelligence or genetic manipulation.

It is of course problematical whether the Prometheus Project can really be carried through successfully in twenty-five to fifty years. Some unforeseen problems are likely to arise, but the only way we can know for sure is to try it and see.

The Prometheus Coordinating Agency

I have suggested a number of functions for the PCA, so I feel it incumbent on me to describe a structure and mode of operation for this agency despite the fact that I am not well equipped, either by talent or inclination, to do so. Many of the remarks I have to make here are about things that should be avoided, rather than things that should definitely be present.

The PCA must fill a number of roles in its work, in all of which it must work to keep the search for goals from becoming an agent of disunity among men, or a vehicle by which a small group can impose its will on the rest of mankind. Clearly, the fulfillment of these roles will be no easy matter, unless there is widespread support for the activities among all men.

One indication of such support would be the willingness of talented people to take an active part in the formation and workings of the PCA. These will obviously require a variety of abilities. I think that, as far as possible, the staff of the PCA should be people who are actively interested in the Prometheus Project, rather than professionals in various fields who would look on their work for the PCA as just another job. One should not underrate enthusiasm as a factor in accomplishing difficult ends. As the Project goes on, it may become necessary to include more professionals for specific jobs, such as poll taking, but perhaps some of these could be subcontracted to outside agencies.

The amount of time people in the PCA devote to its work will obviously be an individual matter. Since the method of financing of the Project is questionable, there will probably be no salary, especially at the beginning. Therefore, the staff of the PCA will need other means of support.

Assuming that the right people are attracted to the PCA, what kind of structure should it have? For obvious reasons, it should be an independent agency rather than sponsored by some government, with a staff not drawn disproportionately from a few national, racial, or economic groups. This may be unavoidable at the beginning because of the greater exposure the idea will have in the developed countries, but every effort should be made to diversify the staff later on.

In its early stages, the PCA will be simply a number of people interested in furthering the Prometheus Project, and need not have any formal structure at all. A structure should be built up gradually as developments require it. The first groups needed would be planners to map out the course of the Project and publicists to spread the word of it. These two subdivisions will persist throughout the life of the PCA. In the second and third stages people who can do philosophical and scientific analyses of goals and field workers who can maintain contact with the many discussion groups will be needed. Still later there will have to be opinion analysts to interpret the preliminary polls and the votes.

While the PCA is being created, the decisions about how it should proceed will be made by its creators and the planners of the Project, but these men should not necessarily be allowed to make decisions indefinitely. The planning group should convince others of the soundness of their plans, rather than order them to carry them out. An organization devoted to producing a unified effort from mankind should at least ideally be intellectually unified itself. Whether an organization can so operate in reality is another matter. As with many of the newer aspects of the Prometheus Project that may seem too idealistic, it has never been tried.

There are good arguments against having one

person as head of the PCA. A man in such a position would face immense temptation to slant the Prometheus Project toward whatever group goals he personally favored. There is no question of ulterior motives involved here; one man is necessarily an atypical sample of humanity, and there should be safeguards against one man's bias being converted into humanity's will.

Since the best-functioning human institutions have had a single man making the ultimate decisions, the PCA would probably function more efficiently with an overall director. But it is sometimes better to sacrifice efficiency to principle, and I think this is one of the cases. Mankind must realize that it as a group is responsible for selecting its goals, rather than having them handed down to it. Any element of structure tending to interfere with this realization must be avoided if possible. Since the PCA itself might also come under this injunction, extreme vigilance is called for to ensure that its work is always coordination, rather than determination.

Instead of a single director for the PCA, another system should be considered. The divisions that carry out specific functions, such as publicity, can make most of their own decisions. When interdivisional matters arise, or when there is conflict, this could be decided by a board with a rotating rather than permanent membership, chosen from all the divisions. To achieve the continuity of principle of a permanent leadership, every effort should be made to explain the principles on which any decision of the board is based throughout the organization. A set of over-lapping terms in office might also be used, as in the U. S. Senate, to ensure some continuity of the personnel involved in making these decisions.

I imagine the PCA not as a tightly knit organization, but rather as a loose grouping of men who wish to devote their efforts to helping the human race choose its long-range goals. The first people who take up this challenge will have their own ideas about how to organize themselves and may opt for a different structure than I have indicated here. The only point I consider essential, and therefore worth repeating, is that the aim of the PCA is to channel the effort of humanity to choose its goals, not to choose the goals for it.

How Can We Get Started on the Prometheus Project?

At present there is no agreement among the human race on its long-range goals. The disagreements between men that threaten to bring about catastrophe in the form of nuclear war refer only to the short run, and the ultimate aims we are pursuing are given little thought. Even if our instinct for survival enables us to avoid thermonuclear disaster, we must still face the challenge of decisions about technological advance. These decisions may come sooner rather than later. Advances in biology appear to be making the option of biological engineering possible before it was expected by even the most imaginative prophets. If we were satisfied with the present or past human condition, we might consider trying to halt or roll back the advance of technology, but, even if this were possible, it does not seem to be humanity's will to freeze our lives in their present imperfect state.

There is no time to lose in beginning the Prometheus Project if it is to help us make decisions about which technological roads to follow and be of aid in avoiding the thermonuclear war that nobody wants. If the time scale described above is roughly accurate, then, if we begin immediately, the final agreement on goals still cannot be expected before the twenty-first century, by which time some of the major technological advances requiring decisions will almost certainly have been made. If we delay the start of the Project very long, the goals we choose may come too late to help in some of the decisions.

How are we to begin? The first step is for those who are convinced by the ideas in this book, or who have reached similar conclusions independently, to make some contact, to establish that some men at least are interested in the search for goals and to produce some alternative ideas about the best way to carry out the search.

Of necessity, the original appeal of a book is to the intellectual community. But I would hope that within a fairly short time—certainly before the PCA is formed—interest in the Prometheus Project would have spread beyond the intellectual community. It is of great importance that political leaders in various countries react sympathetically to it, or at least do not oppose it actively, so that when the PCA begins its work of publicizing, there will be a minimum of government resistance. Political leaders who wish to become involved in it, however, should do so as private citizens; and there is ample precedent for this in the work of various humanitarian or religious organizations.

The most important activity for the early supporters of the Project will be to spread the word of it informally to those who would not ordinarily read this book or think of the idea themselves. This will provide some of the broad base of interest necessary to get the Project off the ground, and also give some indication of the problems involved in publicizing it.

I hope that after a preliminary period of one or two years, there will be enough interest so that something more formal can be done, perhaps some kind of convention where there would be a discussion of how best to proceed and steps could be taken to set up the PCA, or some kind of interim organization.

One important question would be the financing. I have not estimated the cost of the program I have outlined, but I think it would be fairly expensive. The first steps, however, might not be, and one of the charitable foundations would perhaps be willing to sponsor them. But, eventually, if the Project is to succeed, it will have to be supported financially by those who are taking part in it, that is the population of the world. The conference could devise suitable forms for financial contributions.

When the conference has met and set up the

PCA, we will be started on the road that will eventually lead to agreement on our common goals. It is therefore of great importance that those of us who wish to bring this about begin working toward such a conference. To do this we must first get in touch with one another. I would be pleased to hear from anyone who has any comments about the ideas expressed here. In particular I would be interested in any suggestions on how the Prometheus Project might proceed more effectively. Only together will we progress toward the vision of unity of purpose that I hope you will all share with me.

L'Envoi

The search for goals described in this book is my expression of ultimate belief in the existence and power of human rationality. It is a part of our finitude that no man controls the forces that have molded the feelings that underlie his moral judgments. Yet it is a part of the glory of being man that we can plan our futures so that our dreams approach reality. There is nothing in the universe we can rely on to consider our welfare except our own reason. There are no gods that watch fondly over us, no master plan that has been imposed on us from outside, and no automatic progress toward a predetermined goal through evolution. In all the world, only man can, and must, care about his fate.

Some of my readers have probably been disturbed by the often naïve solutions I have offered to the many problems that admittedly lie between my proposal and its ultimate realization. These solutions are highly tentative. I have not written this book because I believe that all these detailed problems are solved, but rather to persuade you of these simple truths. If we grasp the chance to direct our future course, we can use our remarkable scientific and technological accomplishments to transform human life into something wonderfully new and nearer to our heart's desire than anything that has existed before. To do this, we must know what it is we want to be, and act upon it. If we do not, technology will transform us all the same, but in ways we cannot predict and almost certainly will not desire. The challenge is as plain as that, and I have firm faith that mankind will accept it.

This book is much more optimistic about what man can rationally do to determine his fate than most contemporary statements. This is probably because, as a scientist, I have studied and taken part in the most obviously progressive of all human activities. But more objectively I believe that, in the respects that matter most, the course of human history until now has been generally upward. For the future, I agree with William Faulkner, who was neither scientist nor optimist, when he said, "I believe that man will not merely endure, he will prevail."

Notes

I. THE NEED FOR
LONG-RANGE GOALS

1. An interesting presentation of how this might be done is given in Chapter 32 of the book *Intelligent Life in the Universe,* by I. Shklovskii and C. Sagan, Holden-Day, Inc., San Francisco, 1966.

2. See Olaf Stapledon, *Last and First Men,* in the collection of his writings, *To the End of Time,* Funk and Wagnalls Co., New York, 1953.

3. See for example the discussion in Karl Popper's *The Open Society and Its Enemies,* Princeton University Press, Princeton, 1950.

4. Some of the more optimistic views of the possibility of producing artificial intelligence are given in the collection *Computers and Thought,* edited by E. A. Feigenbaum and J. Feldman, McGraw-Hill Book Co., New York, 1963.

5. The molecular biologists and geneticists have been particularly clear about this. See for example *The Control of Human Heredity and Evolution,* edited by T. M. Sonneborn, The Macmillan Co., New York, 1965; *Genetics and the Future of Man,* edited by J. D. Roslansky, Appleton-Century-Crofts, New York, 1966; and the article "Portents for a Genetic Engineering" by R. D. Hotchkiss, *Journal of Heredity,* vol. 56, no. 5, p. 197.

II. WHERE WE STAND

1. J. D. Watson, *The Molecular Biology of the Gene,* W. A. Benjamin, Inc., New York, 1965, p. 67.

2. It cannot be stressed too strongly that the aim of physics is to understand all phenomena in the world, and not just a restricted set. If new phenomena were discovered which required new laws of physics for their description, physicists would rejoice, even if the laws were quite different from

previous ones. The changes in physical law that were necessary to describe atomic processes were very far-reaching, and to some physicists extremely distasteful, but they were made, and the result was a deeper synthesis of physical phenomena.

3. It is suggested by science, but not yet proven, that consciousness can be explained by physics and chemistry. The unraveling of the connection between mind and matter may be the primary scientific problem of the next century. It is conceivable that some surprises are in store for us here. In any case, it is clear that our physiological and physical attributes strongly influence our mental processes, and that changing the former would lead to changes in the latter. This is what is most important for our present purpose.

4. One form of this view is the "argument from design" for the existence of God, given by St. Thomas Aquinas in *Summa Theologica*, question 2. More modern versions are found in H. Bergson's *Creative Evolution*, and E. S. Russell's *The Directedness of Organic Activities*. These works accept the evidence for biological evolution, and try to show that this implies the existence of some plan directing the evolution. A critical analysis of these ideas is to be found in *The Meaning of Evolution*, by G. G. Simpson, Yale University Press, New Haven, 1960.

5. Experiments of this sort were done by R. D. Hotchkiss in 1948. See his Harvey Lecture, Series 49, pp. 124–44, New York, 1955.

6. B. F. Skinner, *Walden II*, The Macmillan Co., New York, 1948.

7. Some experiments on these effects are described by J. Olds in his article "Pleasure Centers in the Brain," *Scientific American*, October 1956; and by E. von Holst and U. von St. Paul in their article "Electrically Controlled Behavior," *Scientific American*, March 1962.

8. A negative appraisal is given in the book *Nightmare Drugs*, by Dr. D. Louria, Pocket Books, New York, 1966. This may be contrasted with the strongly positive attitude toward drugs of many who use them, such as is expressed by Dr. T. Leary in *L.S.D.—The Consciousness-Expanding*

Drug, edited by D. Solomon, G. P. Putnam's Sons, New York, 1964.

9. This is discussed in detail in my article "Ordinary Matter," in *Scientific American,* May 1967.

10. See, for example, the book *Extrasensory Perception,* edited by G. E. W. Wolstenholme and E. C. P. Millar, Little, Brown, Boston, 1956; in particular the articles by D. J. West and J. F. Nicol.

11. See the work of M. Ryzl on improving ESP through hypnosis, reported in the *Journal of Parapsychology 26,* 237 (1962).

12. B. F. Strehler in his *Time, Cells and Aging,* Academic Press, New York, 1962.

13. By intelligent life, I mean life with intelligence at least comparable in quality to human intelligence, i.e., more intelligent than any other species on earth now.

14. The history of astronomy can in many ways be read as the successively deeper recognition of this principle. Some thinkers, such as Aristarchus and G. Bruno recognized it very early. But in some ways it has still not gained general acceptance. Hence the objections that have been raised by many eminent scientists to the existence of any extraterrestrial life, let alone intelligent life.

15. See Shklovskii and Sagan, *op. cit.,* for a discussion of several of these proposals.

16. This attitude is described by Sophocles in *Oedipus at Colonus,* lines 1225–1238. It is not uncommon among literary men up to the present.

17. Here also Sophocles can be quoted as an early example. See his *Antigone,* lines 332–383. A well-known proponent of this view was Condorcet. In the contemporary world, it is perhaps most common among scientists.

18. See for instance B. Russell, in "A Free Man's Worship," reprinted in *Mysticism and Logic,* Doubleday & Company, Inc., Garden City, N.Y., 1957.

19. R. Browning in "Andrea del Sarto."

20. See "The Sermon at Benares," quoted in *The Teachings of the Compassionate Buddha,* edited by E. A. Burtt, New American Library, New York, 1955.

21. This is reported by R. Benedict in *Patterns of Culture,* New American Library, New York, 1946.

22. For instance, W. LaBarre, in *The Human Animal,* University of Chicago Press, Chicago, 1954.

23. St. Paul, *First Epistle to the Corinthians,* XV, 26.

24. See J. P. Sartre, *Existentialism and Humanism,* Methuen and Co. Ltd., London, 1948.

25. "If God didn't exist, everything would be possible," F. Dostoevski in *Crime and Punishment.*

26. This view goes back to J. Locke, in *An essay Concerning Human Understanding,* Oxford University Press, London, 1924.

27. S. Freud, *Civilization and Its Discontents,* The Hogarth Press, London, 1951.

28. D. Riesman, in *The Lonely Crowd,* Doubleday & Company, Inc., Garden City, N.Y., 1953.

III. SOME ROADS THAT WILL BE OPENED

1. This was the case for the Industrial Revolution in England, but not necessarily in other countries such as Japan, where industrialization came later. It would be very useful to study the conscious motivations and expectations underlying such derivative industrialization. This could provide some insight into our own future dealings with technological advances.

2. For example, there is the American Academy of Arts and Sciences Commission on the Year 2000, part of whose conclusions are published in the Summer 1967 issue of the magazine *Daedalus.* Another example is *The Year 2000* by Herman Kahn and Anthony J. Weiner, The Macmillan Co., New York, 1967.

3. Many ludicrous examples of attempts to predict the limits of technology can be cited. Rather than doing so here, I refer the reader to the excellent book *Profiles of the Future*, by Arthur C. Clarke, Harper and Row, New York, 1962, whose first two chapters contain an analysis of some such efforts. The book then goes on to make some rather optimistic guesses about the future of technology. I suspect however that even Clarke's optimism will fall short of the reality.

4. The phrase biological engineering seems preferable to the more standard genetic engineering, since not all the manipulations to be done will be genetic. Biological engineering has been used in a slightly different sense by E. I. Tatum in his article in Roslansky, *op. cit.*

5. This possibility is discussed in detail in some of the articles mentioned in footnote 5 of Chapter I. See in particular the article by Hotchkiss, and the articles by Tatum and Pontecorvo in Sonneborn, *op. cit.* A suggestion of some of the technical difficulties in accomplishing this are given in the article by Muller in Sonneborn.

6. This view is expressed by Corliss Lamont, in his book *The Illusion of Immortality*, Frederick Unger, New York, 1965.

7. Notable examples are *Slan*, by A. E. van Vogt, Dell Publishing Co., New York, 1951; and *Dragon's Island*, by J. Williamson, Simon and Schuster, New York, 1951.

8. Some recent cases are an editorial in *Science*, August 11, 1967, by M. Nirenberg, and a following letter by J. Lederberg in *Science*, October 20, 1967.

9. See William James, *The Varieties of Religious Experience*, New American Library, New York, 1958.

10. A summary of progress along these lines up until 1963 is given in the collection *Computers and Thought*, edited by E. A. Feigenbaum and J. Feldman, *op. cit.*

11. This point of view is described in detail by the psychologist G. A. Miller in his article "Thinking Machines—Myths and Actualities" in *The Public Interest*, Winter 1966.

12. A recent statement to this effect by one worker in the

field is that by Marvin Minsky in his article "Artificial Intelligence" in *Scientific American*, September 1966.

13. Some applications of miniaturized electronic circuits to computers are described in the article "Integrated Computer Memories," by J. A. Rajchman, in *Scientific American*, July 1967.

14. This is an important part of the Puritan ethic, and is responsible in some measure for the opposition to such proposals as the guaranteed annual wage. An analysis of this link is given by J. Galbraith in *The Affluent Society*, Houghton-Mifflin Co., Boston, 1958.

15. The view that knowledge of the personality of the artist may have an important influence on one's reaction to a work has been stressed to me by Dr. Joel Pincus.

16. A. Einstein, Herbert Spencer Lecture, 1933, published in *Ideas and Opinions*, New York, 1954.

17. For example, in the United States the death rate between ages fifty-five and sixty-four has decreased from 27 per thousand per year in 1900 to 17 per thousand per year in 1964. The death rate for people over eighty-five has decreased from 260 per thousand per year to 200 per thousand per year in the same period. Roughly speaking, the death rates at a given age in 1964 are about equal to those at an age ten years younger in 1900. These figures refute some writers who have stated that medical progress has affected the death rate only among young people. The source for the figures quoted here is the report "Vital Statistics of the U.S. for 1966."

18. See B. Strehler, *op. cit.*, chs. 4 and 5.

19. Evidence for a fixed life span of individual cells and their descendants has been given by F. Sinex, as reported in *Perspectives in Medicine and Biology 9*, 208 (1966).

20. Some of the earlier theories are described in B. Strehler, *op. cit.*, chs. 4 and 8. The "genetically programmed" theories of aging are discussed in an article in *Scientific Research*, August 1966, p. 24.

21. An interesting set of such negative reactions were expressed in letters to the *Saturday Review*, in their issue of

November 3, 1956. The letters were in response to an article by Dr. L. Kubie, entitled "Hidden Brain Power," in the October 13, 1956, issue. This article suggested that an extension of the human life span by a sizable factor might soon become possible, and remarked that we would do well to think about how society should react to this.

22. B. Strehler, *op. cit.*, p. 112 *et seq.*

23. A description of the remarkable achievement of Rodia is given on p. 72 of *The New Yorker* for May 29, 1965, by C. Trillin. However, to best appreciate it, one must see the towers themselves, in the Watts District of Los Angeles.

24. See the essays in *The Meaning of Death,* edited by Herman Feifel, McGraw-Hill Book Co., New York, 1959.

25. B. Russell, "A Free Man's Worship," *op. cit.*

26. There are some 10^{80} atoms in the visible universe. The human body contains about 10^{28} atoms. Therefore 10^{52} people would use up all the matter in the universe. There are now about 10^9 humans, so that an increase by a factor of 10^{43}, or 2^{140}, is required for this. At a doubling rate of every forty years, this would take only 5600 years.

27. This argument has been given by Dr. Arnold Faden, in private discussions.

28. See the discussions in I. Shklovskii and C. Sagan, *op. cit.*

29. See for instance F. J. Dyson, as quoted by J. Bernstein in *A Comprehensible World,* p. 72, Random House, New York, 1967.

30. An interesting expression of this is the story "Unite and Conquer," by T. Sturgeon, in the magazine *Astounding Science Fiction,* October 1948.

31. For example, Dr. D. Louria in his article "Cool Talk About Hot Drugs" in *The New York Times Magazine,* August 6, 1967, argues that way.

IV. A CLASSIFICATION
AND ANALYSIS OF GOALS

1. As suggested by Karl Marx in unpublished writing.

2. *The Rubaiyat* of Omar Khayyam, translated by E. Fitzgerald, quatrain 108, second edition.

3. This has been argued recently by K. Lorenz, in his work *On Aggression,* Harcourt, Brace and World, New York, 1966.

4. See for example the discussions of the Zuñi, and the Plains Indians in R. Benedict, *op. cit.*

5. In *Faust,* act I, scene IV.

6. See the section "The Early Scriptures of Buddhism" in *The Teachings of the Compassionate Buddha,* edited by E. A. Burtt, New American Library, New York, 1955.

7. The views of Mahayana Buddhists are summarized in the section "The Mahayana Religious Ideal" in E. A. Burtt, *op. cit.*

8. Particularly the Zen school of Buddhism. See the book *Zen Buddhism,* by D. T. Suzuki, Doubleday & Company, Inc., Garden City, N.Y., 1956.

9. "For what shall it profit a man, if he shall gain the whole world, and lose his own soul?" Mark 8:36.

10. This view is particularly characteristic of Islam, and of many forms of Christianity. Other religious groups emphasize belief more than actions.

11. Although a majority of Americans state that they believe in an afterlife, there is little indication that this influences either their life on earth, or their attitudes toward death. This is probably the case in most, but not all, cultures.

12. The Book of Job, Chapters 38–41.

13. See for example *The Critique of Pure Reason* by Immanuel Kant, E. P. Dutton and Co., New York, 1934.

14. Teilhard de Chardin, *op. cit.*

15. G. B. Shaw in *Man and Superman,* Penguin Books, Baltimore, 1952, describes the need for biological modification of man through selective breeding, but apparently feels that this will be accomplished through the subconscious, since he believes that men will consciously oppose this.

16. W. James, *The Varieties of Religious Experience,* New American Library, New York, 1958.

17. W. T. Stace, *The Teachings of the Mystics,* New American Library, New York, 1960.

18. See the article "Visual Pigments in Man," by W. A. H. Rushton, in *Scientific American,* November 1962.

19. One place where this goal is stated explicitly is in the United States Declaration of Independence, especially in the second paragraph.

20. See for example H. J. Muller, *Freedom in the Modern World,* Harper and Row, New York, 1966.

21. This interpretation of the views of Socrates is given by A. E. Taylor in *Socrates,* Doubleday & Company, Inc., Garden City, N.Y., 1953.

22. See R. Benedict, *op. cit.,* especially the discussion of the Kwakiutl.

23. The negative attitude of some upper-class Romans toward having children is recounted by J. Carcopino in *Daily Life in Ancient Rome,* Yale University Press, New Haven, 1940.

24. The birthrate in Hungary, for example, is about thirteen per thousand per year, or about 25 percent of what it is in Paraguay. Obviously, environmental influences are involved here.

25. M. de Condorcet, *Sketch for a Historical Picture of the Progress of the Human Mind,* Noonday Press, New York, 1955.

26. M. de Condorcet, *op. cit.,* section 10.

27. This view was perhaps justified by the recognition of the

many institutions existing at the time which acted to suppress progress. It seemed natural that if these were removed, progress would automatically follow. This view is often taken by those who would modify a given social institution.

28. A summary of these views is given in H. Spencer, *Social Statistics,* Robert Schalkenbach Foundation, New York, 1954.

29. See for example Julian Huxley, in the chapter "Evolution, Cultural and Biological," from his book *New Bottles for New Wine,* Harper and Brothers, New York, 1957.

30. Democritus, as quoted in *The Greek Atomists and Epicurus,* p. 178, by C. Bailey, Russell and Russell, Inc., New York, 1964.

31. Quoted by Teilhard de Chardin in *The Phenomenon of Man, op. cit.*

32. See the article "The Split Brain in Man" by M. S. Gazzaniga, *Scientific American,* August 1967.

33. For example, F. Hoyle in *The Black Cloud,* Harper and Brothers, New York, 1957.

34. O. Stapledon, *Odd John, Last and First Men, The Star Maker,* in the collection *To the End of Time,* Funk and Wagnalls, New York, 1953; *Death into Life,* in *Worlds of Wonder,* Fantasy Publishing Co., Los Angeles, 1949.

35. This is especially treated in *Death into Life, op. cit.*

36. *Last and First Men,* Chapter 15, *op. cit.*

V. PHILOSOPHICAL PROBLEMS IN SETTING GOALS

1. Examples of this are the world religions, such as Christianity, Islam and Buddhism. Also some political movements such as Marxism.

2. See *Goals for Americans,* Prentice-Hall, Inc., Englewood Cliffs, N.J., 1960.

3. For instance, a country born from an anticolonial revolution is likely to have the elimination of colonialism as one

of its goals. A country, such as Spain, which originated in a religious conflict may make the spread of the successful religion one of its goals.

4. *Brave New World,* by A. Huxley, Bantam Books, New York, 1953, outlined a society in which the members were conditioned, starting even before birth, to fit the roles they were to play in the society. The idea goes back to Plato's *Republic.*

5. See A. C. Clarke, *Profiles of the Future, op. cit.,* for some remarks on this.

6. I have in mind here continuous governments such as England since 1688, some of the Chinese dynasties, and periods of the Roman Catholic papacy. In all cases known to me, there have been substantial changes after several centuries, either inside the institution, or from the outside.

7. In the United States the budget of the Federal Government is now about 150 billion dollars out of a gross national product of 750 billion dollars. Other industrialized countries have similar percentages.

8. This is indicated by the fact that quite diverse societies can claim they are following the same principles. For example, Sweden and Spain both claim to be Christian countries. Also, China and Romania both say that they are following Marxist principles.

VI. THE PROMETHEUS PROJECT

1. See *Elmtown's Youth,* by A. B. Hollingshead, J. Wiley and Sons, New York, 1949, for a description of some of these methods.

2. That is, by requiring less effort or contribution from people, we might still be able to reach the same goal, only more slowly.

3. See K. Arrow, *Social Choices and Industrial Values,* J. Wiley and Sons, New York, 1963, for a discussion of the difficulties in determining preferential ordering.

General References

R. BENEDICT—*Patterns of Culture*, New American Library, New York, 1946

H. BOORSE and L. MOTZ—*The World of the Atom*, Basic Books, New York, 1966

A. C. CLARKE—*Profiles of the Future*, Harper and Row, New York, 1962

F. CRICK—*Of Men and Molecules*, University of Washington Press, Seattle, 1966

E. A. FEIGENBAUM and J. FELDMAN—*Computers and Thought*, McGraw-Hill Book Co., New York, 1963

W. JAMES—*The Varieties of Religious Experience*, New American Library, New York, 1958

T. JUKES—*Molecules and Evolution*, Columbia University Press, New York, 1966

O. KLINEBERG—*Social Psychology*, Henry Holt and Co., New York, 1940

D. SCIAMA—*The Unity of the Universe*, Doubleday & Company, Inc., Garden City, N.Y., 1959

I. S. SHKLOVSKII and C. SAGAN—*Intelligent Life in the Universe*, Holden-Day, Inc., San Francisco, 1966

B. F. SKINNER—*Science and Human Behavior*, The Macmillan Co., New York, 1953

T. M. SONNEBORN—*The Control of Human Heredity and Evolution*, The Macmillan Co., New York, 1965

B. F. STREHLER—*Time, Cells and Aging*, Academic Press, New York, 1962

W. SULLIVAN—*We Are Not Alone*, McGraw-Hill Book Co., New York, 1964

J. D. WATSON—*The Molecular Biology of the Gene,* W. A. Benjamin, Inc., New York, 1965

V. WEISSKOPF—*Knowledge and Wonder,* Doubleday & Company, Inc., Garden City, N.Y., 1962

ANCHOR BOOKS

Government and Political Science (continued)

ANCHOR BOOKS

ANTHROPOLOGY AND ARCHAEOLOGY